PREFACE

This report presents the findings and recommendations of an independent Public Inquiry into the Foot and Mouth Disease (FMD) epidemic that occurred in Cumbria in 2001. The Inquiry was conducted under the umbrella of the Cumbria FMD Task Force and was supported and facilitated by the Cumbria County Council.

In preparing the report we have sought to set out the essential background and key facts about the epidemic, to provide objective comment on events and to highlight matters which might influence future policies and strategies in relation to FMD. Within our terms of reference, we have also attempted to address the issues raised with us in evidence, or in discussion at our public meetings.

Cumbria is a unique area of the UK, rich in landscape heritage and biodiversity, and outstanding in its natural beauty. In 2001 it was also unique in the scale and duration of the FMD that occurred. It was at the epicentre of the epidemic that ravaged the UK, and was the location of approximately 44% of all the farms that were infected. So far as we are aware, Cumbria was also the first example in the world of a large FMD epidemic occurring in a highly diversified rural area, where agriculture and tourism are each major components of the economy. Not only was agriculture affected by FMD, there was a huge impact on tourism.

Many people in Cumbria suffered great hardship and distress as a result of FMD, and even now, over nine months after the last case was reported, there is a continuing legacy of the events that took place. However, there are also significant signs of recovery and regeneration, and amongst the many people we met during the Inquiry there is a clear determination to ensure that Cumbria will flourish in the future.

We are grateful to the Cumbria County Council for its support and encouragement during the course of our work. We also wish to thank the Recorders for their work in capturing the detailed evidence given during the Public Hearings. We owe a particular debt of gratitude to the Secretariat of the Inquiry who unstintingly dealt with the collection and cataloguing of written evidence, the arrangements for oral evidence and public meetings, and much more. Most of all, we offer our sincere appreciation to the people of Cumbria who contributed so fully and constructively in helping us to understand the events and issues of the 2001 epidemic. Within our report it has not been possible to detail all the accounts and information we received but each piece of evidence was important in helping our understanding and in allowing us to develop our findings and frame recommendations.

The 2001 FMD epidemic was a catastrophe for Cumbria. The threat of a future outbreak is unlikely to diminish but we believe that the events of 2001 must never be repeated.

Cumbria Foot and Mouth Disease Inquiry Panel, August 2002.

Howard Christie   *Philip Hancock*
Jan Darrall   *John Hetherington*
Derek Ellwood   *Andrew Humphries*
David Etherden   *Canon Geoffrey Ravalde*
Nick Gent   *Phil Thomas (Chairman)*

CONTENTS

PART 3. ECONOMIC, ENVIRONMENTAL AND SOCIAL IMPACTS

EXECUTIVE SUMMARY

1. In 2001 the UK experienced probably the most serious epidemic of Foot and Mouth Disease (FMD) ever to occur in a previously FMD-free country. Almost from the start the epidemic was widespread; there were outbreaks from the North to the South of England, in Southwest Scotland, in Wales and in Northern Ireland. The disease was first detected in mid-February and the last outbreak was confirmed at the end of September. During the intervening period 2,026 outbreaks were recorded in Great Britain and 4 in Northern Ireland.

2. Cumbria in Northwest England was at the epicentre of the epidemic. It suffered 893 outbreaks and was the second longest affected area. The County, which is rich in natural heritage and scenically beautiful, has livestock farming, tourism and outdoor recreation amongst its economic mainstays. The effect of FMD was therefore devastating.

3. In addition to the infected farms, a further 1,934 farms were subjected to complete or partial animal slaughter as part of the disease control and eradication measures. Restrictions on livestock movements also impacted on non-infected farms, resulting in livestock management problems and economic losses. As a result of restrictions on public access to the countryside, tourism, outdoor recreation, public amenities and some public services were also badly affected.

4. The disease eradication policy of livestock destruction on both infected and 'exposed' farms required a massive scale of slaughter and animal disposal, and there were problems in implementation of disease control, communication and other measures. These led to an upsurge of public concern over the way that the epidemic was being handled.

5. When the epidemic had been brought under control and recovery of the economy established, the Cumbria FMD Task Force and Cumbria County Council considered that there were important issues that needed to be reviewed as a basis for the development of future policy. It was concluded and that these would be addressed best through an independent Public Inquiry with terms of reference to consider:

- the outbreak and control issues
- advice, communication and local and central relationships
- organisational and capacity issues
- impacts on the wider Cumbrian economy
- aftermath, recovery and regeneration
- recent policy developments and future strategies.

This is the Report of that independent Public Inquiry.

6. The Report is in four Parts. The Introduction provides the necessary background to the disease and to the national policies, and developments in policies, for its control and eradication. Part 2 deals with the FMD epidemic that occurred in Cumbria, focusing on issues related to its control and eradication. Part 3 examines the economic, environmental and social impacts of the disease. Part 4 considers the future, and particularly the development of the Cumbria Rural Action Zone (RAZ) programme.

7. Almost inevitably, given the nature and unprecedented scale of the 2001 epidemic, the disease control measures adopted by the UK Government were complex. Policies and strategies were adjusted to deal with the emerging situation, and both the legal requirements and implementation on the ground were subject to continual change in order to address problems as they developed. The Government's submission to the national 'Lessons to be

Learned' Inquiry conducted by Dr Iain Anderson, and the recent National Audit Office report, give a step by step account of events and decisions that were taken as the epidemic progressed. This conveys the impression of a considered and measured response to an escalating animal disease crisis, and recognition that there were some limited problems.

8. In contrast, on the basis of the evidence gathered in Cumbria, we found that on the ground there had been confusion, disorder and delay. In a few cases this was attributed to failures or errors on the part of individuals. However, in the majority of cases, we encountered appreciation and praise for the dedication and hard work of the personnel who were actively engaged in dealing with the crisis. But, we found widespread dissatisfaction with the 'system' and with many operational aspects of the disease control and clean-up measures.

9. Against this background we have considered organisational structures and resources locally in Cumbria, as well as matters of communication both locally and with central government structures. We have then turned our attention to movements of livestock, disease spread, biosecurity and the disease control and eradication procedures, including the policies of 3km-zone culls and contiguous premises culls. We have also considered the use of vaccination to assist in disease control.

10. Even making full allowances for the almost unique circumstances that arose during the 2001 FMD epidemic in Cumbria, we were disturbed by the range of systems and communications failings that were identified during the Inquiry. A lack of appropriate contingency planning, and a failure to adhere to some of the provisions in the contingency plan that existed, compromised the FMD disease control campaign from the outset. This was made worse by the insularity of the local Animal Health Office and by a failure to adopt a multi-agency approach in shaping its early response to the disease. Things did improve in later March but the measures effected then should have been in place sooner.

11. We have concluded that it is no longer sensible to consider FMD wholly in isolation from other areas of emergency planning. The devastation the disease can bring is now fully apparent, and after 11 September 2001 bio-terrorism must be regarded as an additional risk factor. We accept the rationale of the decision made by Cumbria County Council to await a lead from MAFF/DEFRA, and not to open the County's Emergency Centre. However, we believe that in planning for a future multi-agency response the Emergency Centre should be considered as a 'hub' facility. This should be agreed with DEFRA within the framework of contingency planning.

12. Speed of response in halting animal movements and in making decisions to cull infected animals or dangerous contacts is crucial in getting on top of FMD, and the evidence suggests that in the early phase of the 2001 epidemic there were delays that should have been avoided. There are also indications that the length of the Cumbria epidemic reflected a failure in the application of the slaughter strategy that was adopted.

13. We also set out our concerns over issues of biosecurity and the problem of developing improved biosecurity against a background of uncertainty about the detailed epidemiology of disease spread. The scale of the outbreak in 2001 was enormous but, as yet, there is little evidence that the epidemiological data that has been collected is providing new insights which will help to develop improved disease control strategies.

14. An integrated risk-based strategy for FMD is outlined, taking account of the experiences of the 2001 epidemic. This addresses the themes of prevention, planning, prompt response, premeditated tactics and prepared recovery measures, each of which could be separately evaluated as part of an overall defence strategy. We recommend that Government establish an independent Working Party to develop an integrated risk-based strategy using this type of

approach.

15. In line with the importance of agriculture and tourism, FMD reduced the economy of Cumbria by an estimated £266m, or approximately 4% of the GDP of the County. Income loss to agriculture was approximately £130m, equivalent to 41% of the normal total livestock output of the County. Indirect effects on the wider economy through agriculture were about £30m, two-thirds of which related to the effects on the animal feed industry. However, compensatory payments to farming for compulsory slaughter of livestock provided a positive cash flow into the County's agriculture of some £90m.

16. The economic impact on tourism varied substantially with the type of tourism business and its location. However, total revenue was reduced by some £200m, with a further indirect effect of £60m on the wider economy. In the worst affected areas in June 2001 turnover was reduced by two-thirds, causing some business virtually to cease trading. The effect on jobs appeared largely 'absorbed' by reduced recruitment of summer workers and by 'under-employment' of workers who were not eligible for unemployment benefit or did not register as unemployed for other reasons.

17. Various government schemes were introduced to ease the burden on businesses during the crisis. Those providing rates and taxation relief or deferments of payments were well received. State Aid constraints on the structure of the Business Recovery Fund, channelled through the Regional Development Agency, limited its usefulness. It would have been better if greater flexibility in the application of the funding could have been exercised. A range of charitable organisations and local voluntary groups undertook excellent work in meeting local needs. Considerable leadership was provided through the Cumbria FMD Task Force, which was brought together under the initiative of the County Council.

18. Carcass disposal by landfill, mass burial or burning on pyres raised a range of environmental problems and exposed significant shortcomings in communication and liaison between central government departments/national agencies and the local Departments of Environmental Health and Public Health. Some of the methods of carcass disposal that were adopted raised significant local issues that should be avoided in any future outbreak. These have left a legacy of community concern, particularly in respect of the future of the mass burial site at Watchtree, near Great Orton.

19. There was considerable evidence of the impact of the FMD outbreak on community life in rural Cumbria and on aspects of emotional, social and mental health. These effects are difficult to quantify on a population basis but results of ongoing research, with a study group of 54 people from a range of occupations, give cause for concern. Some 20% of the group are reporting signs of post-traumatic experience and 11% are being treated for clinical depression or anxiety.

20. Based on the work of the Rural Regeneration Team of the Cumbria FMD Task Force, proposals have been advanced for the creation of a RAZ programme. This covers broadening the base of the rural economy, renewing and strengthening tourism, developing and enhancing agriculture, promoting environmental sustainability, and delivering social and community regeneration. The programme, which is in the final stages of consideration for additional Government funding, is highly innovative in approach and has the potential to become an international exemplar in co-ordinated rural development. We have considered the economic development aspects of the programme, and the needs for programme implementation in agriculture, tourism and other areas of business, and made specific recommendations.

21. We believe that the Social and Community Regeneration programme will go some considerable way to re-establishing the community frameworks and networks that have been

damaged or lost during the FMD epidemic. However, we have concerns that there are deeper societal effects that may be difficult to address.

22. During our collection of evidence we became conscious of repeated underlying themes related to the remoteness of central government from farming practice and the rural way of life. All sectors of the community expressed disenchantment with the political system and felt they had been let down during the FMD crisis. This seemed symptomatic of a growing distrust and community alienation.

23. The challenges facing agriculture and the rural areas of Britain are difficult to overestimate. However, reflecting Britain's population distribution, urban issues often dominate political priorities. There is a need to find ways of raising awareness and understanding of rural agendas and for public policies to be formulated from a practical understanding of the problems that need to be addressed.

LIST OF RECOMMENDATIONS

Foot and Mouth Disease in Cumbria

PLANNING RESOURCES AND MANAGEMENT

Contingency Planning

1. We recommend that DEFRA undertakes a comprehensive revision of its draft contingency plan in the light of the findings of this and other FMD Inquiries. The plan should be conceived on a multi-agency basis and should engage all the relevant agencies, including the County Councils. In local FMD planning, the Cumbria County Council Emergency Centre should be considered as a 'hub' facility for any future multi-agency response (page 52).

Resources

2. We recommend that DEFRA, in conjunction with partner organisations and veterinary practices throughout Cumbria, reviews personnel requirements (both numbers of personnel and provision of preparatory training) as part of its contingency planning process. Likewise, the local Contingency Plan should specify clearly the stage and scale of epidemic that will trigger a request from DEFRA for assistance from the Army (page 52).

Movement Restrictions

3. We recommend that, in any future outbreak, movement restrictions are introduced as soon as the first case is diagnosed and that provisions are introduced to deal with animals in transit. Additionally, local authorisation of action in dealing with an outbreak should be introduced as early as possible, with DEFRA headquarters kept fully informed of decisions (page 53).

Risk analysis

4. We recommend that DEFRA's risk analysis documents be reviewed from time to time and revised as necessary. A statement of the risk of spread of FMD (or other diseases) through the carriage of particulate matter from pyres should be added. Also, in conjunction with the other agencies with statutory, enforcement or health responsibilities, DEFRA should published a risk analysis of all the carcass disposal options, include computer modelling of the consequences of breakdown in biosecurity in any phase of the elected disposal strategies (page 53).

Outstanding Disputes and Payments

5. We recommend that, as a matter of priority, DEFRA resolves all outstanding disputes and settles all financial accounts relating to the FMD epidemic in Cumbria by 31 March 2003 (page 53).

Epidemiology

6. We recommend that DEFRA commissions an external review of its provision of epidemiological support in connection with FMD, and of the usefulness of the data collected to the understanding of disease spread (page 53).

BIOSECURITY

Import Controls

7. We recommend that the Government publish performance targets and annual performance statistics in respect of import controls in order to promote public confidence in the new measures that have been introduced (page 54).

Livestock Movements

8. We recommend that the current 'standstill' regulations continue to be reviewed to identify practical policies for increased biosecurity that will be more compatible with the needs of commercial farming systems. Through its agencies Government should ensure the provision of training courses for farmers on biosecurity and disease recognition (page 54).

Biosecurity Research

9. We recommend that DEFRA commissions research on biosecurity to provide a robust understanding of the biosecurity measures appropriate to safeguard against FMD spread. The cost benefit of public funding for preventative biosecurity measures in the event of a FMD outbreak should be examined (page 54).

FMD DEFENCE

Developing an Integrated Strategy

10. We recommend that Government establish an independent Working Party to develop an integrated risk-assessed strategy for defence against FMD, covering prevention of disease entry to the Britain, contingency planning, response to disease detection, tactics for disease control and eradication, and post-outbreak recovery (page 56).

Economic, Environmental and Social Impacts

COUNTRYSIDE ACCESS

Implementation of Legislation

11. We recommend that, as a matter of policy, all changes by Government in disease control legislation requiring implementation by Local Authorities should be supported by appropriate risk-assessment guidance (page 79).

Veterinary Risk Assessment

12. We recommend that there should be closer co-ordination in the veterinary risk advice that is provided nationally by Government and regionally through the SVS Animal Health Offices (page 79).

Period Restriction on Path Closures

13. We recommend that in any future disease outbreak, any general legal declaration covering the closure of footpaths or land by the County Council should be made on a strictly time-limited basis, for example 28 days (page 80).

Responsibility for Path Closures

14. We recommend that the appropriate Local Authority (the County Council where that applies) should hold sole responsibility for closures of Rights of Way, or other pathways, under the Foot and Mouth Order 1983, replacing the present arrangements whereby powers are held both by the Local Authority and DEFRA (page 80).

Enhancing Access

15. We recommend that Cumbria County Council build on the work of the Restriction Review Team to establish regular meetings between responsible bodies and key stakeholders to develop methods and policies to protect and enhance countryside access (page 80).

ECONOMIC IMPACTS

Task Forces

16. We recommend that, where appropriate, Cumbria County Council build on the FMD Task Force model and create similar, but smaller, groups to help take forward initiatives related to the County's post-FMD recovery and regeneration (page 80).

Tourism Insurance

17. We recommend that tourism organisations advise the industry of the limitations of existing insurance cover and, together with the NWDA, make representations to the insurance industry for the development of policies that would provide cover in the circumstances that occurred in Cumbria in 2001 (page 80).

Economic and Employment Planning

18. We recommend that there should be a programme of research to provide an improved understanding of the relationship between economic activities and the creation of jobs in the Cumbrian economy (page 81).

State Aid Rules

19. We recommend local and central government campaign for greater flexibility in State Aid Rules to allow specific economic emergencies, such as those that occurred in Cumbria in 2001, to be addressed (page 81).

Regional Economic Monitoring

20. We recommend that the NWDA and Cumbria County Council build on existing initiatives to establish an intensive programme of regional economic monitoring that will provide the detailed up-to-date data necessary to allow business support initiatives to be targeted to the needs for economic regeneration (page 81).

ENVIRONMENTAL IMPACTS

Environmental Forum

21. We recommend that Cumbria County Council seek to establish a forum in which the public sector agencies covering environment and health would meet on an annual or more frequent basis. This would be designed to create closer links between the different service

providers and to develop an integrated plan for Cumbria covering the areas in which the national and local bodies have responsibilities, including FMD contingency planning (page 81).

Disposal Sites

22. We recommend that the operators of the Distington landfill and of the Watchtree mass burial site build on existing initiatives to ensure that complaints of smell or other environment intrusions on the local community are fully addressed (page 81).

23. We recommend that DEFRA states unequivocally the future plans for the Watchtree site, and particularly whether it is to be permanently closed for disposal of animal carcasses or other waste. Permanent closure would be the plan favoured by the local community and the Inquiry Panel endorses that view (page 82).

Buried Waste

24. We recommend that Cumbria County Council, the Environmental Health Departments, Environment Agency and DEFRA jointly consider what might be done to map where materials are buried on farms and, where necessary, to address any safety issues that may emerge (page 82).

COMMUNITY AND HEALTH IMPACTS

Health Research

25. We recommend to both researchers and funding bodies that there should be further work into the emotional, social and mental health consequences of FMD in Cumbria, and that the research should be extended to encompass children (page 82).

Looking to the Future

RURAL ACTION ZONE (RAZ)

International Exemplar

26. We recommend that the RAZ should be promoted internationally as an exemplar of good practice in rural development (page 93).

Cumbrian Projects and Partnerships

27. We recommend that at the earliest possible stage the Rural Regeneration Company establishes a publicly accessible database of all the projects and partnerships operating in Cumbria, with outline details of the work being undertaken (page 93).

BUSINESS DEVELOPMENT

Agricultural Development

28. We recommend that 'participative research' techniques be evaluated as a means of project implementation, and that an 'Agricultural Strategy Committee' is established as an interface between the RAZ organisation and the farming industry (page 93).

Tourism Forum

29. We recommend the formation of a Cumbria Tourism Forum, with an independent Chair from the private sector, to facilitate the different sectors of the industry in co-ordinating funding bids related to the RAZ programme (page 93).

Cumbria Institute

30. We recommend that the concept of a 'Cumbria Institute' be explored with a view to advancing the development of higher education, research and consultancy in Cumbria (page 94).

COMMUNITY DEVELOPMENT

Rural Agendas

31. We recommend that within the RAZ programme there should be a Rural Agendas project designed to facilitate community action and leadership on rural issues (page 94).

PART 1. INTRODUCTION

In 2001 the UK experienced a massive epidemic[1] of Foot and Mouth Disease (FMD). The scale was unprecedented. It was the most serious epidemic ever to take place in the UK, and probably the worst ever to occur in a previously FMD-free country. Almost from the start the epidemic was widespread; there were outbreaks from the North to the South of England, in Southwest Scotland, in Wales and in Northern Ireland.

The disease was first detected on the 20 February and the last outbreak was confirmed on the 30 September. During the intervening 32-week period, 2,026 outbreaks were recorded in Great Britain and 4 in Northern Ireland. As part of the disease control policy there was slaughter and disposal of susceptible animals from infected farms and from farms considered to have been exposed to infection. Not including newborn animals, which were unrecorded, some 4 million livestock were destroyed in the eradication programme and a further 2.5 million under the related schemes to deal with animal welfare and marketing problems.

The epidemic led to a countrywide ban on animal movements and to widespread restrictions on public access to the countryside. Coupled with the media images of animal slaughter and disposal, the restrictions on access and freedom of movement brought many businesses in affected areas almost to a halt - tourism and all types of outdoor recreation were particular badly affected.

FMD in Cumbria

The effect of the FMD epidemic in Cumbria was devastating. Firstly, the County, which is rich in natural heritage and one of the most scenically beautiful areas of Britain (Appendix 1), has livestock agriculture, tourism and outdoor recreation as economic mainstays. It was the epicentre of outbreak, suffering 893 FMD cases[2] - almost 44% of the UK total - and was the second longest affected area. The first case was reported on 28 February 2001 and the last on 30 September 2001.

Secondly, the disease eradication policy of livestock destruction on both infected and 'exposed' farms impacted massively on the scale of the slaughter and disposal. The numbers of animals concerned was enormous – approximately 1,087,000 sheep, 215,000 cattle, 39,000 pigs and over 1,000 goats, deer and other animals. In addition to the 893 infected premises, a further 1,934 were subjected to complete or partial animal eradication. Approximately 45% of Cumbria's farm holdings were subject to animal culls and, in the North of the County where the epidemic was most severe, this figure rose to 70%. Moreover, because of the scale of the epidemic, the disease control measures impacted on every farm in the County causing major disruptions in livestock management, attendant problems of animal welfare and damaging economic losses.

Lastly, they were problems in implementation of disease control, communication and other measures. These led to an upsurge of public objection and to expressions of public concern, frustration and anger at the way that the epidemic was being handled. Individuals and communities felt that they were being unconsidered or poorly served by the authorities, and there was a loss of confidence in the government department leading the control and eradication process. That was the Ministry of Agriculture, Fisheries and Food (MAFF) until 8 June when the Department of Environment and Rural Affairs (DEFRA) was formed, absorbing MAFF in the process. During the Inquiry we found the public regarded DEFRA and MAFF as synonymous, irrespective of whether referring to events before or after 8 June. Therefore, unless it was otherwise stated, we have adopted a similar approach and our general references to DEFRA should be taken to include MAFF[3].

It might be thought unexceptional that a community faced with a FMD epidemic of the scale and duration experienced in Cumbria would be concerned and upset. However, that would fail to grasp the strength and depth of emotion in Cumbria at the time, or the lasting legacy of the FMD epidemic. During this Inquiry witnesses have told us that at the height of the epidemic, some communities of Cumbria were close to the point of violence[4], and we can attest to the strong emotions that remain.

As has already been indicated, the Cumbria FMD epidemic did not affect only agriculture and on-farm businesses, it quickly had implications for businesses and individuals throughout the County. Tourism and recreation businesses were almost immediately affected and there was a rapid escalation of impact into all types of businesses in the service and supply sectors. Individuals were confined to their properties, schools and public services were disrupted, social events were cancelled, and meetings of clubs and societies ceased. Everyone in the community was affected, many people substantially so.

Early in March 2001, the Cumbria County Council decided to bring together key individuals and organisations. Their objective was to achieve co-ordination of action and maximise the local, regional and national impact of efforts to mitigate the wider economic and social effects of the epidemic. This led to the establishment of the Cumbria FMD Task Force, which has played a key role throughout the epidemic and the post-epidemic recovery period. The Task Force established a Steering Group to co-ordinate activities, and a series of specialised sub-groups. These included groups on: Business Survival; Restrictions Review (Footpaths); Market Expansion; Tourism Marketing; Health and Social Care; Special Landscapes; Voluntary Funding; and Communications.

The Cumbrian community was active in seeking solutions to the immediate problems of FMD and in beginning to plan for the longer term when the epidemic would be passed and there would be a need to rebuild the County's economy. Various initiatives stemming from the Task Force's activities and campaigning are considered later in this report. However, particular mention should be made of the Cumbria Rural Action Zone (RAZ) programme which represents a genuinely trailblazing initiative to bring together the full range of resources and capabilities of the government agencies to provide a co-ordinated approach to the future development of rural Cumbria.

Government Inquiries

The weekly incidence of FMD outbreaks in the UK peaked around 25 March 2001 and by May had fallen very considerably. However, there was a substantial 'tail' of infection until the last case on 30 September 2001. Although a small number of path closure orders remained to be officially lifted, the disease problem can be regarded as having concluded by 5 February 2002. At that time the EU Standing Veterinary Committee agreed that export of meat products from the UK could be resumed, after the Office International des Epizooties (OIE) had confirmed that the UK had regained its FMD free status.

As the epidemic was brought under control there were calls for a Public Inquiry into its origins and the way that it had been handled. However, the Government determined that a better and quicker approach would be to establish independent committees to look into different issues relevant to the epidemic. Thus, on 9 August 2001 two UK-wide inquiries were announced. These were:

- the inquiry into the lessons to be learned from the foot and mouth disease outbreak of 2001 (Chaired by Dr Iain Anderson)[5]; and

- the scientific review by the Royal Society of questions relating to the transmission, prevention and control of epidemic outbreaks of infectious diseases in livestock. (Chaired by Sir Brian Follett)[6].

Additionally, at the same time, the Government announced the establishment of a Policy Commission into the Future of Food and Farming (Chaired by Sir Don Curry – the 'Curry Report'). This Commission, which reported in January 2002[7], was to consider future policies and strategies for the development of farming in England. It paralleled the corresponding reviews - *A Forward Strategy for Scottish Agriculture*[8] and *A New Direction for Farming in Wales*[9] - commissioned by the devolved administrations during 2001.

Cumbria FMD Inquiry

The decision of the Government not to institute a full Public Inquiry into the FMD epidemic raised concerns in a number of English Counties that opportunities to learn from the experiences and difficulties of the 2001 epidemic would be lost. It was recognised that there was a need to draw a line under the past, and to bring closure for the communities affected by the epidemic. But it was also felt that there were important aspects of disease control strategy, clean up operations, public access and recovery, and regeneration of the economy that needed to be reviewed as a basis for the development of future policies[10]. In the light of this, Cumbria County Council Leader Rex Toft, Chairman of the Cumbria FMD Task Force, announced that Cumbria would have its own FMD Inquiry, details of which were published on 21 March, 2002.

From the outset, it was decided that the Inquiry Panel would consist of an independent Chairman and members selected to provide a balance of relevant experience, rather than having any representational role or particular affiliation (Appendix 2). In the context of the 2001 FMD epidemic in Cumbria, the Inquiry's terms of reference were to consider:

- the outbreak and control issues
- advice, communication and local and central relationships
- organisational and capacity issues
- impacts on the wider Cumbrian economy
- aftermath, recovery and regeneration
- recent policy developments and future strategies.

The Inquiry Panel, ably supported by a Secretariat (Appendix 2), provided by the Cumbria County Council, was free to decide on the way in which the Inquiry would be conducted, and determined to adopt a five-strand approach. This consisted of:

- a wide public invitation for the submission of written evidence;
- sixteen half-day sessions of formal submissions of oral evidence;
- ten half-day sessions of meetings with representatives of groups, organisations and businesses;
- six 3-hour public meetings; and
- visits to Longtown Market and the Watchtree (Great Orton) and Distington disposal sites, and viewing of Halburn and Hespin Wood sites.

Throughout the Inquiry every attempt was made to make the proceedings open and accessible and to provide opportunities for all those who wished to give evidence. Formal evidence sessions were held at Kendal and Carlisle, and were transmitted live to the BBC Cumbria Internet site. Most witnesses presenting oral evidence were invited by the Inquiry but at the completion of each session there was a 30-minute 'forum' in which anyone in attendance could make a submission. Meetings with representative groups, organisations and businesses were arranged at various locations to facilitate attendance, and the public meetings were held at 6 locations in different parts of the County. They were well advertised and well attended.

A summary of the sources of evidence submitted is given in Appendix 3 and Appendix 4; in total there were over 140 written submissions, evidence was taken formally or informally from some 100 people, and the public meetings had an attendance of over 700. Additionally, the Panel considered a range of 'core documents'. Many of these were in the public domain or were supplied by the County Council or others. In line with the its policy for 'local inquiries'[11], DEFRA did not accept our invitation to present oral evidence but was helpful in responding to questions which we submitted and in supplying supplementary papers. A number of documents prepared by the Government were available on the Internet and these were helpful in our analysis and deliberations.

During the course of the Inquiry we have considered a large volume of evidence and documents. However, in our report we have made a conscious decision to present a succinct summary of the relevant background material and of our findings and recommendations, rather than a descriptive account of the material presented to us. We have provided numbered text notes and references which are included at the end of the report; these should be read as part of the report itself. The written evidence submitted to the Inquiry and the transcripts of the oral evidence are to be archived by the Cumbria County Council so that a permanent, and publicly available, record of the material will be maintained.

In our investigation, analysis and report we have made every attempt to establish, and confirm, matters of fact, and to present the available evidence as clearly as possible. In some cases we have dealt with matters of personal recall or opinion; where appropriate we have noted the evidence source of the statements we report. Our intention throughout has been to gain understanding and to identify the lessons to be learned, rather than to bask in the wisdom of hindsight or seek apportionment of blame.

The Inquiry was conducted under the umbrella of the Cumbria FMD Task Force and supported and facilitated by the Cumbria County Council. However, some of our recommendations reach beyond that constituency and have wider implications. Where appropriate, we have put these into context and have indicated those to whom the recommendations are directed. We would, nonetheless, emphasise that our investigations and conclusions are based on the 2001 FMD epidemic in Cumbria, as distinct from any other areas of the UK[12]. Whilst we have necessarily considered some matters of science in relation to FMD we restricted our deliberations in the knowledge that a full scientific review of FMD, amongst other diseases, was being undertaken by the Royal Society.

FMD in the UK

This section of the report provides an overview of the 2001 UK FMD epidemic, as a background to our later consideration of FMD in Cumbria. It deals with the nature, origin and spread of the disease and with animal health aspects of the national policies and control provisions. The account is based on various sources of information. However, on matters of policy, strategy and disease control, we have drawn substantially on: the Government's submissions to the Anderson Inquiry[13] and the European Parliament's Temporary Committee[14]; the Report of the Comptroller and Auditor General[15]; and the report of the Chief Veterinary Officer (CVO) on the origin of the epidemic[16].

CHARACERISTICS OF THE DISEASE

FMD is caused by viruses of the Picornaviridae family, genus *Aphthovirus*; there are seven immunologically distinct serotypes, and more than 60 sub-types of virus. The disease is one of the most contagious known to affect cloven-hoofed animals. Cattle, pigs, sheep, goats and deer are susceptible and may exhibit symptoms after an incubation period of only 1 to 5 days. Although the disease is not of significant risk to humans, it is one of the most economically devastating animal diseases in the world. Clinical signs vary in severity between species. They include fever and blister-like lesions on the tongue and lips; in the mouth, muzzle and snout; on the teats; and between the toes. The condition is rarely fatal, except in young animals but cattle and pigs may exhibit severe clinical signs with substantial suffering, anorexia and a loss of productivity.

The virus is excreted in breath, saliva, faeces, urine, milk and semen; and can remain active in the tissue of infected animals unless the acidity falls to below pH 6. Transmission of the virus can occur through contact between animals or by indirect 'contacts' created through animals of any species or through physical objects. Thus the virus can potentially be passively transmitted by man or other animals, or by contamination of vehicles, equipment, clothing etc. Airborne transmission has also been reported, and this is a special problem with infected cattle and pigs, which can emit a substantial 'plume' of infection in their breath.

The effective dose for transfer of infection from one animal to another varies with the virus strain, the species of animal and the route of infection. The respiratory route requires a much lower dosage than the oral route, and cattle and sheep are more susceptible than pigs. However, the differences in susceptibility may be academic in practice because of the high infectivity of the virus.

ORIGIN OF THE 2001 FMD EPIDEMIC

FMD was introduced to the UK from overseas but its precise origin and route of entry into the country may never be known. The virus was of the Type O, PanAsia strain, similar to that which caused an outbreak in South Africa in 2000. However, in the past decade the strain has occurred in many countries, producing disease outbreaks in India, Turkey, Greece, Bulgaria, Bangladesh, China, Taiwan, South Korea, Mongolia, Russia, Japan and several areas of the Middle East. This has led to warnings of the potential risk of the virus to EU countries[17]. Other strains have been responsible for FMD outbreaks in South America, and in several regions of Africa, other than the Kwazulu-Natal region of South Africa.

The first indication of FMD in the UK was gained through the alertness of a Meat Health Service Officer who detected signs in a pig at an abattoir in Essex on 19 February. Disease was confirmed on 20 February, and this led to a search for the 'index case' involving some 600 livestock tracings. By 23 February FMD had been confirmed at a pig-finishing unit at Burnside Farm, Heddon-on-the-Wall in Northumberland, which was licensed to feed processed waste food under the Animal Byproducts Order 1999.

Detailed investigations carried out on 24 February by staff from the National and World FMD Reference Laboratory, Pirbright revealed that the majority of pigs at the farm were infected with FMD, but were at different stages of infection. On the basis of expert opinion some of the pigs had 12-day-old FMD lesions, which implied that the infection could have been in the unit as early as 26 January. Indeed since pigs had been sent to slaughter on 8 and 22 January it is possible that the infection may have been present earlier.

The CVO reports that all possible means for the introduction of FMD into Burnside Farm have been investigated and that introduction by animals, people, vehicles, equipment, vermin and wildlife have been ruled out. He also comments that there was no evidence of disease on premises within 3km of Burnside Farm that pre-dated that discovered on the farm itself. Thus, on the basis of epidemiological evidence and a consideration of the risks of potential routes of infection (Table 1), the CVO has come to three main conclusions.

Table 1. Risks associated with routes of introduction of virus into UK and transfer to animals.

Routes	Risk appraisal
Airborne	Unlikely: no outbreaks in nearby countries.
Live animals	Low risk: no live susceptible species imported from countries that have had FMD within 2 years or have undertaken vaccination within 1 year.
Semen	Low risk: country freedom from FMD required, plus semen held in quarantine to check status of donor. Illegal import possible but no desirable genetics in infected countries.
Embryos	Very low risk for the same reasons as semen. Pig embryo transfer not common for technical reasons.
Vehicles	Low risk that contaminated vehicles would come to the UK directly from countries affected by the relevant FMD strain.
Footwear	Low risk from normal footwear. Increased risk where boots or wellingtons could carry contaminated organic material from infected animals to susceptible species. Virus could survive for up to 14 weeks in winter.
People and clothing	Low risk unless direct contact with infected animals within 72 hours of entering UK. Virus could be carried on unwashed clothing for up to 14 weeks, but is cleared from nose and throat after 28 hours.
Hides, skins	Low risk. Treatment required for legal importation would safeguard against introduction of virus.
Milk or milk powder	Generally low risk. Dilution factor in producing bulk milk and subsequent pasteurisation reduces any infectivity. In unpasteurised and refrigerated milk the virus will survive up to 15 days, but infection would depend on reaching susceptible animal. Temperature treatment reduces risk with milk powder.
Meat products	Negligible risk from legal or illegal imports if fully processed as: treated and hermetically sealed; deboned and heated to 70° C; deboned and matured for 9 months; deboned, subject to pH < 6. However, virus will survive in partially cured products such as bacon or air-dried meat for up to six months.
Meat	Risk varies with country or region of origin, livestock species and cut of meat. FMD virus is inactivated in 48 hours in muscle held at 4° C where the pH falls below 6. Post mortem pH changes in pork are less than in beef or sheepmeat. Virus will survive for at least 5 months at 4° C in bone marrow and lymph nodes and longer if carcass is frozen.
	Legally imported meat will be certified as coming from an FMD free country or region. If from a vaccinating country or region only deboned matured beef permitted. Legal imports have not taken place from any country where the Type O, PanAsia strain occurs apart from South Africa. This is improbable as a source because of regulation of importation.
	Illegal meat is of highest risk from countries with FMD and if on the bone or with lymph nodes attached. Deboned meat, especially pork, also presents a risk but there is a greater likelihood of detection of larger consignments in refrigerated containers.
	Personal imports, whether legal or illegal, are less likely to enter the catering chain than commercial imports.
Waste food	EU and UK law prohibits the feeding of catering waste from ships and aircraft to animals. Such material is collected under DEFRA licence and disposed of by incineration or landfill. Other UK catering waste could be safely fed to pigs if processed under the conditions of the Animal Byproducts Order 1999 (but this has now been banned since 24 May 2001). Failure adequately to process infected catering waste would allow survival of the FMD virus and infection.

Note: Adapted from the CVO report on the *Origin the UK Foot and Mouth Disease in 2001*. DEFRA (2002).

Firstly, that Burnside Farm was the index FMD case. Secondly, that the virus was likely to have come from a commercial-scale illegal import of meat or meat product, which was used in a catering outlet from which waste was incorporated into improperly cooked pig feed. Thirdly, although almost identical, the UK virus was unlikely to have been derived from the South African outbreak. Rather it is thought that both the South African outbreak and the UK outbreak were likely to be due to a virus source in the Far East.

The CVO's report also comments on some alternative theories as to the origin and time of appearance of FMD in the country, which have been subject to media and public speculation. The report states:

- only the Institute of Animal Health Laboratory and the Merial Biological Laboratory (for vaccine production) at Pirbright are licensed to hold FMD virus - contrary to suggestions that FMD was released or stolen from the Defence Evaluation and Research Agency or the Centre for Applied Microbiology and Research, Porton Down;
- all food imported for the Army must comply with EU and UK regulations, and that whilst the Army has imported beef from South America, incidences of FMD in that region have not been due to a PanAsia strain of virus;
- laboratory tests conducted by French authorities had failed to confirm the hypothesis that FMD positive sheep were exported from the UK prior to 1 February;
- the CVO of Canada had refuted claims that Canada had known about the presence of FMD in the UK prior to February 2001;
- suggestions that DEFRA or MAFF staff had knowledge of the presence of FMD in the country before its discovery on 19 February were incorrect.

SPREAD OF DISEASE

On the basis of the epidemiological evidence, the CVO's report concludes that the disease spread from Burnside Farm by two routes. The first route related to the transfer of pigs to slaughter on 8 and 15 February and to the subsequent mechanical or personal transmission of the virus from the abattoir to holdings in Essex. This produced an 'Essex cluster' of outbreaks but these made only a small contribution to the national epidemic.

By contrast the second route was much more important. This appears to have involved the airborne transmission of virus from Burnside Farm to sheep at a nearby farm at Ponteland and the subsequent sale of 16 of these sheep on 13 February. The sheep entered the market chain and went via Hexham Market, Longtown Market and through dealers, contaminating sheep, people and vehicles so that the FMD virus became distributed widely through England, Wales and parts of Scotland. Epidemiological investigations of the 2,026 FMD outbreaks that occurred has concluded that they were due mainly to local spread after the initial introduction of FMD into an area. None were found which pre-dated Heddon-on-the-Wall.

This pattern of initial spread of FMD via sheep, which were transported throughout Britain, was a crucial feature of the 2001 epidemic. DEFRA epidemiologists have estimated that by the 20 February when the first pig had been confirmed positive in Essex, 57 farms in 16 counties had been 'seeded' with infective doses of the virus. Moreover by 23 February, when the farm at Heddon-on-the-Wall had been identified as a potential source, there were 62 infected farms in 23 counties. Thus, from its early infancy, the epidemic was set to ravage the country, and this was reflected in the later widespread distribution of cases (Appendix 5).

REGULATION OF FMD CONTROL POLICIES

The regulation of FMD control in the UK operates under a framework of European Union (EU) and domestic legislation. The EU policy on the control of FMD is set out in Directives

85/511/EEC as amended by Directive 90/423/EEC, whilst the domestic legislation is covered largely by the Animal Health Act 1981 and the Foot and Mouth Disease Order 1983 (as amended).

Under the European Directives each Member State is required to respond to an outbreak of FMD by introducing biosecurity measures, including restrictions on the movement of livestock, people and vehicles, and by instituting a policy of slaughter of animals to 'stamp out' the disease. With this in view, Directive 90/423 requires each Member State to have a contingency plan showing its proposals for dealing with at least 10 simultaneous outbreaks of FMD.

In UK, the Animal Health Act 1981 states the relevant Government Minister may cause to be slaughtered any animals affected by FMD or suspected of being affected or any other animals that appear to have been exposed to infection. It also requires owners to be recompensed for their loss of livestock. Alongside this, the Foot and Mouth Disease Order (with any amendments that may be made to it as required) sets out the rules to be followed in respect of areas subject to disease control restrictions and infected premises.

Overall, Member States are required to operate their FMD control measures under the terms set down by European Commission decisions, which are advised by the EU Standing Veterinary Committee. During the 2001 epidemic, missions of the EU Food and Veterinary Directorate were carried out in the UK on the 12-16 March, 23-27 April, 30 April-4 May and 20-24 August and their findings and advice reported[18].

DISEASE CONTROL

Almost inevitably, given the nature and unprecedented scale of the 2001 epidemic, the disease control measures adopted by the UK Government were complex. Policies and strategies were adjusted to deal with the emerging situation, and both the legal requirements and the implementation on the ground were subject to continual change in order to address problems as they developed. The Government's submission to the Anderson Inquiry provides a 'blow by blow' account of the epidemic and of the Government's responses at each stage. Some of the decisions and detailed policies are considered later in our report; in the following paragraphs we have sought simply to set out the main features of the national control framework and of how it was adjusted over time.

Organisation and Management

Animal health is a partially devolved area of authority in Great Britain. The Scottish Executive has responsibility for policy development and implementation in Scotland; the Welsh Assembly has more limited responsibility for operational matters in Wales; and DEFRA has responsibility for England and for any non-devolved matters. In practice the system can be considered relatively seamless because of the overarching national role of the State Veterinary Service (SVS) - which reports to DEFRA - and because of a series of concordats between the DEFRA, SVS and the devolved administrations.

Under the FMD Contingency Plans for Great Britain, endorsed by the European Commission in 1992[19], responsibility for the control of FMD rests with the Minister of Agriculture, who delegates responsibility for the control direction and strategy to the CVO. The CVO, in turn, arranges for national disease control to be co-ordinated through a Departmental Emergency Control Centre (DECC) and effected through the 23 Animal Health Divisional Offices of the SVS in England, Wales and Scotland.

In circumstances of a FMD outbreak, a SVS Office acts *inter alia* as a local Disease Control

Centre (DCC), headed by a Senior Veterinarian and reporting to the national DECC. With this in view, each of the Offices is responsible for developing its own local FMD contingency planning. This process is assisted by Chapter 3 of the SVS's internal *Veterinary Instructions, Procedures and Emergency Routines*, which provides a detailed account of the actions and procedures that should be adopted in the event of a FMD outbreak.

In line with the national contingency plans MAFF took the initial lead in directing and co-ordinating the Government's response to FMD. However, as the national scale of the epidemic became clear, the Prime Minister, with the Cabinet and the Minister for Agriculture, began to oversee the development of policy. Close to the height of the epidemic on 22 March, the Cabinet Office Briefing Room (COBR) was opened, and it continued in use until September. Disease control strategy and operations (but not policy) during this period were directed by the COBR committee, consisting of representatives of all relevant departments and agencies[20], and chaired by the Prime Minister or Secretary of State for Defence, or later by DEFRA Ministers. Reflecting these arrangements the Cabinet Office had a role in the response to FMD from an early stage, and particularly within the COBR framework.

Changes in Organisation and Management

The national DECC was set up on 21 February and put in place a range of actions that were required to be taken during the first weeks of the epidemic. However, by mid-March it was judged that the scale of the epidemic was over-reaching the resources, management and organisational capacity of the SVS and diverting veterinary expertise into management activities not requiring veterinary skills. Thus it was decided to separate veterinary policy and operational functions, both at 'head office' and in the field.

In response, on 14 March, a Director of FMD Operations was introduced alongside the CVO and on 26 March this post became Director of a Joint Control Centre (JCC), incorporating the DECC. In parallel, from 19 March, Regional Operations Directors were introduced alongside Divisional Veterinary Managers in the SVS Offices. These veterinary and administrative posts were regarded as complementary and were tasked with developing integrated operations within the local DCCs on the basis of the most appropriate local model. At the same time, the Army began to be deployed in support of the FMD campaign, and local management arrangements needed to respond to the involvement of the troops.

Scientific Advice

From the start of the epidemic account was taken of the findings and conclusions of the BSE Inquiry[21] on the use and public accessibility of independent scientific advice by Government. At different times, both the CVO and the Chief Scientific Adviser (CSA) consulted groups of independent scientists and veterinarians. In March, at the Prime Minister's request, the CSA established a FMD Science Group consisting of representatives from four teams of UK epidemiologists[22], plus other science specialists, veterinarians and members with experience of FMD control. On the basis of some of the computer models produced by the epidemiologists the CSA advised the Government on 23 March to modify the disease control policies and to introduce what became known as the '24/48 hours contiguous culling policy'.

DISEASE CONTROL SYSTEMS

In accordance with EU and UK law, the principal elements of the disease control strategy in 2001 were:

- controlling movements of susceptible animals;
- introducing biosecurity[23] measures to prevent the spread of disease;

- rapid reporting, identification and diagnosis of infected animals;
- rapid and effective tracing of animals that had been exposed to infection;
- rapid slaughter of susceptible animals on infected premises that had been exposed to the disease;
- disposal of carcasses in a such a way as to avoid risk of spreading FMD virus;
- preliminary and secondary cleansing and disinfecting of premises;
- statistically based serological testing of animals for evidence of current or previous disease to enable restrictions to be lifted safely.

In support of these activities the operational approaches were based on those set out in Directive 85/511/EEC and the UK FMD legislation. Of particular note, was the use of 3km-radius 'protection zones' and 10km-radius 'surveillance zones' in which there were various restrictions on the movements of animals, people and equipment, as well as on other activities, and the introduction of biosecurity measures designed to reduce disease-risk. The main categories of restriction were covered by the provisions for *Infected Area* and *Controlled Area* declarations and by the use of *Forms A, C* and *D*. (*Form B* and *Form E* were used to lift the effects of *Form A* and *Form D*, respectively.)

When disease was first suspected a *Form A* was served on the premises, declaring it to be an *infected place*. No movements were allowed on or off the premises, without permission, and a series of measures was required to establish biosecure isolation of the premises. After clinical examination by a DEFRA vet, who confirmed the suspicion that disease was present, a *Form C* was signed. This prohibited movements of animals within an 8km radius of the place of the suspected outbreak or on any road, rail or motorway passing within 3km, except under licence.

On formal confirmation of the disease by laboratory test or clinical signs, an *Infected Area* was declared, based on a minimum distance of 10km radius. Livestock movements were banned and rigorous biosecurity measures put in place. All premises within a 3km *protection zone* area were placed under *Form D* restrictions. An *Infected Area* designation could be lifted after clinical examination of cattle and pigs and blood testing of sheep within the *protection zone* had proved negative. However, this was not allowed until 30 days after the preliminary cleansing and disinfecting of the infected premises. A *Form D* was given to premises, both within and outside an *Infected Area,* if there were reasonable grounds for suspecting that an animal has been exposed to infection. It imposed a ban on animal movements, except under licence, and introduced a requirement for rigorous biosecurity measures to isolate the premises.

On 23 February, by special Order, the whole of Great Britain was declared an FMD *Controlled Area*. This imposed restrictions on the movement of all animals and carcasses, except under licence, and introduced a range of restrictions on markets, fairs, 'gatherings of animals' and hunting activities. Movements of animals were later permitted, on the basis of the veterinary-assessed risk, to allow the operation of the food chain and to safeguard animal welfare.

At the core of the UK disease control policy was the rapid slaughter of animals on infected premises and animals otherwise considered as having been exposed to the virus. However, the detail of this policy was adjusted as the epidemic progressed, and on the basis of the Government's account could be regarded as having three main phases.

Phase 1 (from 20 February) involved the slaughter of all animals at infected premises and the tracing and consideration for slaughter of all dangerous contacts. Veterinary officers also visited holdings within 3km of infected premises to check for infection.

Phase 2 (from 15 March) began when Nick Brown, then Minister of Agriculture, announced to Parliament new measures to control the spread of disease. These made provision for:

- intensifying surveillance controls within 3km of infected premises;
- slaughtering sheep in 3km protection zones in Cumbria and Dumfries and Galloway;
- slaughtering flocks that had received sheep from Longtown, Welshpool and Northampton markets;
- slaughtering flocks that had received sheep from dealers known to have handled infected flocks.

Additionally, on 21 March, there was increased flexibility for local vets to slaughter on suspicion, and the need for veterinary approval from the DECC before slaughtering could be instigated was removed. There was also a reduction in the required turn round time for 'dirty vets' from 5 to 3 days, and the introduction of standard valuations for stock to speed up the valuation process[24].

Shortly after, on 23 March, the CSA presented new advice taking account of the models that had been considered in the FMD Science Group. Based on this, the Agriculture Minister in a statement on 27 March, confirmed a new 'contiguous culling' policy, and on 6 April instructions were sent to field staff on how it should be implemented. The policy set targets for the slaughter of susceptible animals on infected premises within 24 hours of initial report and the slaughter of animals on contiguous premises within 48 hours. The Minister's statement also outlined proposals for focusing efforts in Cumbria on clearing animals identified for slaughter and on creating a 'fire break' south of the worst affected area[25].

Phase 3 (from 26 April) involved an easing of the contiguous culling policy. Although dangerous contacts and contiguous premises continued to be culled, scope for local veterinary discretion was introduced. This allowed animals to be spared if there was insufficient evidence of exposure to the disease, and excluded the culling of cattle where it was justified on the basis of the prevailing biosecurity. A strictly limited exception was also brought in for rare breeds of sheep and heafed (hefted) sheep[26] of particular genetic merit, subject to arrangements for isolation and biosecurity.

Subsequently, from 24 May, there was a policy change that applied only to Cumbria. There, the slaughter of sheep in the 3km protection zones was yet to be completed and it was decided that serological testing should be undertaken before reaching a decision to slaughter. In the remainder of County (outside the 3km zones) the national policies continued to be applied.

Finally, between 10 October and 18 December, as the epidemic had been brought under control, there were three separate changes in the procedure for 'slaughter on suspicion'. This resulted, at the final change, in 'testing on suspicion' to allow FMD to be confirmed on the basis of laboratory tests on suspect animals.

THE COURSE OF THE EPIDEMIC

Because of the failure of early detection of the presence of virus in the country the 2001 FMD epidemic had a 'head start.' Within 6 weeks the number of reported cases soared to reach almost 300 in a week (Figure 1). By early April, the epidemic was past its peak, and by early-May, 11 weeks from the start, the incidence had fallen to below 50 outbreaks per week. However, the epidemic had a tail of 21 weeks before it was finally stamped out, and the tail accounted for 25% of the total outbreaks.

Almost inevitably, comparisons have been made between the 1967-68 epidemic in the UK and that in 2001. The epidemics were very different in character; the first was locationally confined and occurred largely in cattle, whereas the second was distributed throughout the country and mainly in sheep. However, the number of infected premises in 1967-68 was of the same order as in 2001 (2,364 premises as compared with 2,026) and the two epidemics were almost identical in length, 222 and 221 days.

Figure 1. Number of FMD outbreaks in the UK for the week commencing on the indicated date in 2001.

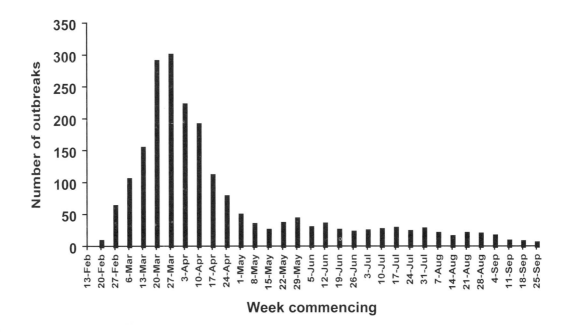

The major difference was in the scale and logistics of the control operations for the two epidemics, in the numbers of animals slaughtered and in the associated disruption and costs (Appendix 6).

PART 2. FOOT AND MOUTH DISEASE IN CUMBRIA

Rather than being a single epidemic, the FMD that was experienced in Britain in 2001 can be regarded as a series of simultaneous epidemics in different parts of the country[27]. Here we have focused on the Cumbria epidemic. Within our terms of reference we have concentrated on matters and issues that were raised during the Inquiry, briefly setting out the background and the range and balance of evidence we received. Where appropriate, we have indicated issues on which there was consensus. As with any Inquiry, it can be argued that the evidence we received was from a self-selecting section of the community. However, we went to considerable lengths to obtain a wide and representative view; and we believe that our objective was largely achieved.

We should also record that in a number of areas our findings paint a very different underlying picture to that outlined in Part 1 of this report. The documents produced by the Government and the NAO convey the impression of a considered and measured national response to an escalating animal disease crisis, and the recognition that there were some limited problems. We, in contrast, found evidence that on the ground there had been confusion, disorder and delay. In a few cases this was attributed to failures or errors on the part of individuals. However, in the majority of cases, we encountered appreciation and praise for the dedication and hard work of the personnel who were actively engaged in dealing with the crisis. Conversely, we found widespread dissatisfaction with the 'system' and with many operational aspects of the disease control and clean-up measures.

To a degree, we accept that there may be different perceptions depending on whether a management and operations system is viewed 'top down' or 'bottom up'. However, we believe that Government and its agencies have a responsibility to provide effective service to the community. In that context, we have identified a number of serious shortcomings we believe should be addressed.

FMD: Management in Cumbria

ORGANISATIONAL STRUCTURES

Immediately FMD occurred in Cumbria, a DCC was established at Carlisle. This was based on the regional Animal Health Office at Rosehill Industrial Estate ('Rosehill'). Under normal circumstances this Office was responsible for dealing with animal health matters in Cumbria, Northumberland, Durham, Tyne and Wear, and Cleveland. During the course of the epidemic, a second DCC was established at Kenton Barr to deal with cases on the east side of the country, but the Carlisle DCC remained the centre of control for Cumbria.

The DCC reported directly to the national DECC, based at the DEFRA Office in Page Street, London ('Page Street') and the management and administrative arrangements in place directly reflected those set out in the SVS manual of *Veterinary Instructions, Procedures and Emergency Routines*. However, after the third week in March, as the structures were changed in Page Street and the JCC was established, a post of Regional Operations Director was established at Rosehill and Jane Brown was seconded to be the first appointment. A little later, after 25 March, an Army contingent under the command of Brigadier Alex Birtwhistle was posted to the area and became an integral part of the disease control operations.

During the Inquiry we were told on numerous occasions that there had been significant improvements in the management of disease outbreaks and in local relationships as the epidemic progressed. A number of witnesses commented favourably on the improvements that had followed the appointment of Jane Brown and the involvement of Brigadier Birtwhistle and his men. There were also criticisms: the organisational changes and additional resources should have been introduced earlier; the periods of secondment of Regional Operations Directors were too short (there were three appointments at different times); and some operational and administrative failures continued to occur right up to the point of disease eradication. However, we recorded the considerable appreciation of the changes that had been made in late March, and noted that evidence on disease control management needed to be evaluated in the context of the stage of the epidemic to which the evidence referred.

RESOURCES

Prior to FMD occurring, the Regional Animal Health Office consisted of the main office at Rosehill plus offices at Kendal and Newcastle. The total complement of staff, consisting of veterinary and non-veterinary grades, was 54.5 posts. However, there were some vacancies at Veterinary Officer and at Administrative Officer/Assistant grades, so that staff in post numbered 47.5, of which 38.5 were at Carlisle (Table 2).

By the height of the outbreak, the staffing had been increased by secondment and appointment and was in total 953. Additionally, there was an Army complement of approximately 130, and a range of externally contracted transport and other services. In short, the escalation of resources was massive, and there were related challenges in quickly providing temporary office accommodation and equipment.

Post FMD the regional areas covered by the Animal Health Offices have been altered to bring them closer into line with the Government Office boundaries. The Carlisle Office now covers Cumbria alone and has a staff complement of 33, which comparatively speaking is higher than prior to the FMD epidemic.

Table 2. Manpower resources at Carlisle in the Regional Animal Health Office (pre-FMD), at the height of the FMD epidemic, and in the restructured Regional Animal Health Office system (post-FMD)[28].

Grade types	Actual (Pre-FMD)	Actual (At height of FMD)	Actual (Post-FMD)
Veterinary personnel	5	218	7
Managerial and executive personnel	9	126	7
Administrative personnel	24.5	165	19
Other personnel	0	444	0
Total	38.5	953	33

Note: Actual post-FMD figures relate to a reduced geographical area compared with pre-FMD figures (see text).

COORDINATION OF EMERGENCY RESPONSE

In most disaster and emergency situations it is usual to establish a local multi-agency consortium, which uses its joint resources to address the tasks of initial response and subsequent recovery. Recognising these needs and in line with their statutory responsibilities, Local Authorities, through their Emergency Planning Departments, prepare both generic emergency plans and a range of specific emergency plans, to cover identifiable local hazards. Typically, emergencies result from some catastrophic event and emergency plans normally identify the lead organisation (usually the Police Force) and the partner organisations that will be involved in the initial response and long-term recovery measures. These plans are developed between the partner organisations, facilitated by the Local Authority's Emergency Planning personnel. They are subject to regular review and updating and to simulation exercises. Many Authorities, including Cumbria County Council, maintain an Emergency Centre, which is resourced with computer and communication equipment and can be 'opened' in an emergency situation.

Excepting those that are particularly hazardous to man[29], animal diseases are outwith the disaster and emergency provisions. They come under the oversight of DEFRA and often require simultaneously to be dealt with at local, national and EU levels. However, within that framework, there is a system of contingency planning and a recognised need for a local contingency plan setting out how DEFRA will engage with partner organisations and what actions will be taken. In the case of animal disease epidemics the 'disaster' builds over the early epidemic phase, but that aside, the principle of a multi-agency response remains a core consideration.

At the first stage of the FMD epidemic a range of partner organisations recognised that their involvement would be required and began to prepare accordingly. We learned that the Environment Agency established its emergency structures almost immediately[30] and that the County Council emergency services set in train their preparations to respond. However, there was a clear view that MAFF/DEFRA was the lead organisation in animal disease matters, and partner organisations expected MAFF/DEFRA locally to initiate and co-ordinate a multi-agency response[31]. In the event that expectation was not fulfilled until several weeks into the epidemic.

There are a number of potential explanations for this, and some on which we can comment. Firstly, whilst we have not seen the FMD Local Contingency Plans for Rosehill, we have studied the FMD Contingency Plans for Great Britain and Chapter 3 of the SVS manual *Veterinary Instructions, Procedures and Emergency Routines* on which the Local Contingency Plan would be based. In our view these documents do not provide sufficient emphasis or detail on the need for multi-agency working. Moreover, we found no evidence that Rosehill had regularly undertaken any FMD simulation exercise on a multi-agency basis. Secondly, we have received evidence that the personnel and management resources of Rosehill were rapidly over-stretched - a view consistent with the speed of development of the epidemic and the appointment of the Regional Operations Director. Finally, we were told by a number of separate witnesses that in their experience MAFF/DEFRA was insular in its attitude to partner organisations and almost secretive in its approach to sharing information.

It is apparent that in the early stages of the outbreak the standing instructions in Chapter 3 of *Veterinary Instructions, Procedures and Emergency Routines* served unreasonably to restrict information[32]. But there are other things that we found more difficult to explain. For example, DEFRA has drawn attention to the fact that at the time of the initial outbreak the National Contingency Plan was not publicly available on an Internet site. In evidence, we were told that, at Rosehill, the Contingency Plan was regarded as internal and confidential. A request from a partner agency to have access to the document, so that responses could be co-ordinated, had therefore been denied.

COMMUNICATION ISSUES

As the Inquiry went on, the quality and effectiveness of communications during the FMD epidemic emerged as a key issue. Because of the scale and complexity of the FMD operations there was need for excellent communications between all those involved:

- nationally between Government/DEFRA and farmers and the general public;
- internally between the DCC and DEC/JCC;
- locally between the DCC and its personnel on the ground;
- locally between the DCC and partner organisations;
- locally between the DCC and farmers and the public;

33

- locally between partner organisations and communities; and
- locally between communities of different interests.

Although there were some notable successes, particularly within the communities, there were regrettably many shortcomings in the communication processes. Even late in the epidemic communication problems were still being encountered.

In the course of the Inquiry we found the most frequent praise was for BBC Radio Cumbria – which was universally considered to have conducted a truly excellent information campaign. Likewise there were plaudits for Border Television and the publications of the Cumberland News Group, whose coverage had been widely appreciated. The most criticism was reserved for the Ministerial Statement on 15 March which, apparently in error, announced that the 3km-zone culling policy would apply to 'animals' rather than to 'sheep'. The distress that this error caused to cattle farmers cannot be overstated. It was a signal event, which for many created a perception that those 'in control' were 'out of touch' or were being disturbingly careless.

We received a range of distressing accounts of poor communication between the authorities and farmers (and others) relating to the culling and disposal of animals. In some instances the approach that the authorities were described as having taken bordered on the totalitarian. We can find no excuse for this, although we readily acknowledge that the pressure of events and the need for the authorities to act quickly created genuine problems. In counterbalance we also received reports of slaughter and disposal operations which were conducted with very sympathetic communication and great consideration for the distress of the farmers concerned. Nonetheless, a significant number of those who spoke to us, particularly at the public meetings, had encountered problems of communication with DEFRA at some stage during the chain of events from their farm being identified for slaughter to payments being received for the livestock destroyed.

We cannot attempt to offer an authoritative analysis of the range of communication problems that occurred during the epidemic, but the subject deserves serious study as a basis for improving government services to rural communities. The following list, which is not in any order of priority, indicates communication areas we noted as being problematic.

- *Communication as a two-way process.* There was, and remains, a sense of frustration amongst the communities of Cumbria that the communication during the epidemic was 'top down'; there was a huge difficulty in communicating to the Government the problems that were having to be endured. This was an issue not only for those in farming but also for the wider rural community[33].
- *Simple Messages.* Government policy for dealing with FMD changed over a short period as the epidemic developed. Some of the disease control issues were complex and, according to perceptions were poorly explained or justified, e.g. 3km-zone slaughter and contiguous cull policy. Additionally, policy implementation was overlapping and partial, creating an impression of disorder[34].
- *Methods of communication.* In accordance with current thinking on communication, the Government Departments placed great emphasis on communication through their websites. This was appreciated by many organisations and individuals who are frequent Internet users. However, it failed to communicate with a large part of the target audience in the farming and rural communities of Cumbria. On the basis of this Inquiry we would conclude that local radio is the most effective route of communication.
- *Consistent information.* We received numerous statements to the effect that the information and advice received from the DCC was often variable, depending on when you phoned and to whom you spoke[35].

- *Communicating with field staff.* At the early stage of the epidemic vets in the field had limited autonomy and communications with Page Street for authorisation of action created delays. Communication with field staff generally presented challenges[36].
- *Adequate communication systems.* Although the contingency plans have instructions for enhancing telephone systems when DCCs are set up, there were many comments from farmers on the difficulties of telephone access to make reports or seek advice.
- *Relevant knowledge.* In dealing with the farming industry, communicators and administrators require a relevant level of knowledge of agriculture and food production. In many instances this appeared to be lacking.
- *Written communication.* Written communication from DEFRA was not always of a high standard. Some letters used unfortunate choices of expression, were not sufficiently clear or appeared threatening[37]. There were instances of poorly photocopied forms that were difficult to read. Also there was evidence of the Department giving verbal instructions or making agreements, which were not confirmed by letter, leading to later dispute[38].

Cumbria's FMD Epidemic

The sheep predicated to have brought the virus from Hexham are reported to have passed through the Longtown Market on 15 February but there was a also a sale on 22 February that could have further contributed to disease spread[39]. The first case of FMD was reported in Cumbria on 28 February. It has now been estimated by DEFRA that before the first case was confirmed there were at least 38 farms in Cumbria seeded with infection.

Figure 2. Number of FMD outbreaks in Cumbria for the week commencing on the indicated date in 2001.

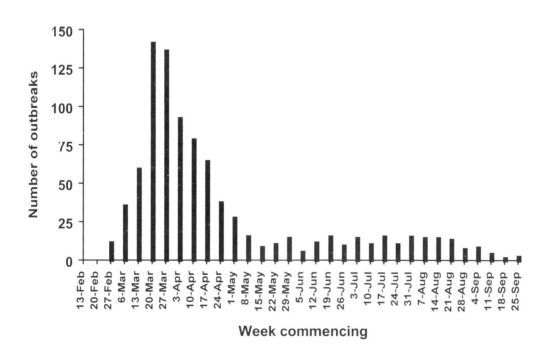

Initially the number of new outbreaks increased dramatically: by 20 March it had reached over 140 per week (Figure 2); by early April it was past its peak and by mid May the worse of the disease looked to be over. However, as in the rest of the UK, the epidemic had a long tail and over a quarter of the outbreaks occurred between the beginning of May and the end of September. In July and August there was a second flare up, which was mainly in the 'Penrith Spur'.

The disease control and eradication strategy adopted was set out in Part 1 of our report. A *Phase 1* slaughter policy was put in place initially. That was augmented after 15 March by the 3km-zone culling of sheep and, in early April, by the contiguous premises culling policy. According to the Government the firebreak cull, announced on 15 March, was never implemented, and the 3km cull and contiguous cull were not fully implemented[40]. However, that apart, the control policies in Cumbria were in principle the same or even greater than those adopted in other parts of Britain. As elsewhere, the stated aim was eradication of FMD by restrictions on animal movements, rigorous biosecurity measures and the rapid slaughter and disposal of infected and potentially exposed animals.

However, the time taken to eradicate the disease in Cumbria was 214 days, one of the longest in the UK. Only, in Northumbria, which recorded about a fifth of the outbreaks, did eradication take longer. Of note is that in Dumfries and Galloway, in Scotland to the north of Longtown, FMD was stamped out in 83 days (Table 3). This is significant because Dumfries and Galloway and Cumbria were separate parts of the same Longtown area of infection.

Table 3. Time to eradicate the disease and number of outbreaks by Disease Control Centre[41]

Centre	Time to eradication (Days)	Number of outbreaks
Newcastle	218	190
Carlisle	214	891
Cardiff	165	101
Leeds	164	140
Stafford	146	72
Preston	140	55
Exeter	112	172
Taunton	101	9
Dumfries & Galloway	83	177
Worcester	73	79
Galashiels	63	11
Leicester	55	9
Chelmsford	51	11
Gloucester	50	85
Truro	35	4
Caernarvon	25	13
Reigate	23	5
Reading	12	2

Note: Dumfries and Galloway was an area of the Ayr Animal Health Office.

By the time that the Cumbria epidemic was over there had been outbreaks throughout a large part of the County mainly concentrated in the lowland areas along the M6 corridor, though Eden and, to the North, through the Allerdale and Carlisle districts. The Southern Districts of Copeland and South Lakeland had only a small number of outbreaks, and the National Parks and the upland areas were relatively unaffected. Barrow-in-Furness District remained disease free (see Appendices 7-10).

Disease Spread

MOVEMENT OF LIVESTOCK

We heard a range of views about the role of sheep movements in the spread of FMD. As a generality, those with farming interests saw significant sheep movements as unavoidable, given the stratified structure of sheep production in Britain and the links between hill and lowland systems. They also accepted that sheep dealers play a role in balancing supply and demand in the marketing chain. Conversely, a number of non-farmers felt very strongly that the FMD epidemic was partly due to poor farming practice and to modern patterns of sheep movement in particular.

In fact, in the Cumbria epidemic, long-distance sheep movements were not an important factor, and sheep movement itself was nothing new. Sheep have been traded throughout the borders of England and Scotland from time immemorial, and without serious disease implications. The critical issue in 2001 in Cumbria was that FMD in sheep brought into the County went undetected until after clinical cases in pigs and sheep started to appear elsewhere. Given the long period for which Britain had been free from FMD and the difficulty of spotting it in sheep, the failure quickly to identify infection in flocks may be understandable. However, it also argues that farmers should be recognised as the front line of the UK's disease defence system, and farmer training and government disease alert services developed accordingly.

As a result of the epidemic, a system of 20-day-period movement restrictions was introduced by the Government to reduce the risk of disease being spread from farm to farm by the movement and mixing of animals. We were told of the practical difficulties and increased bureaucracy that this was creating for the farming industry and the market chain. There are genuine concerns that the '20-day standstill' arrangements are inoperable in the context of a stratified sheep and cattle industry. We note that the recent relaxation of the rules now recognises this.

However, there appears to be complete consensus amongst farmers that an immediate ban on all animal movements should be implemented in the event of any future outbreak of FMD in Britain. There is wide awareness of the epidemiological evidence that if MAFF had imposed an immediate movement ban in 2001, when the first pig was detected in Essex, the number of subsequent cases would have been a fraction of that which occurred. Several farmers and others in the livestock industry pointed out that, if the concept of an immediate movement ban were accepted, consideration would need to be given to animals in transit.

In 2001, because of the time of year, most cattle were housed, but the prohibitions on the movement of sheep across roadways, together with the restrictions imposed as a result of many farms coming under *Form D*, created major animal welfare problems. In some cases these were addressed by slaughter of animals under the Livestock Welfare (Disposal) Scheme or, later in the outbreak, by animal movements approved on the welfare grounds. Not surprisingly strong arguments were made to us for movement bans to be flexible enough to allow for local conditions, and local veterinary risk assessment. There was a strong view that some of the approaches adopted in 2001 had been driven by bureaucratic requirements rather than by common sense.

DISEASE SPREAD IN CUMBRIA

Accepting the present view that FMD entered Cumbria via Longtown Market and was transferred onto farms through the purchase of sheep, the mechanisms whereby it spread to cover half the County are more difficult to unravel. Firstly, it seems that the disease was initially seeded at a large number of locations, so subsequently it must have spread simultaneously from several different points. Secondly, FMD is difficult to spot in sheep so that its first recorded presence may post-date the date of first occurrence in a flock Thirdly, the 3km culls and the contiguous culls served to increase the area of each 'disease location' on the map, so that as the epidemic progressed accurately pinpointing the location of the virus became more difficult.

At the start of the epidemic MAFF set up a Veterinary Epidemiology Unit comprising a headquarters team and field teams in the regions. At its maximum this Unit was 45 people strong, although that is quite small taking into account the size of the epidemic. The CVO's report[42] indicated that each of the Britain's 2,026 FMD cases was subjected to a detailed clinical and epidemiological investigation. And, that the data was used to estimate the age of the lesions at the time of reporting, to evaluate the origin of infection of each farm and to estimate the date on which infection was introduced.

However, in the vast majority of cases it has not proved possible to pinpoint a specific route of transfer of disease between farms, and a high proportion of outbreaks is attributed to 'local transfer'. This is defined as 'spread between infected premises within 3km, which has not been fully determined'. It is attributed to 'aerosol spread between animals in close proximity' and/or 'contamination in an area of an infected place resulting in infected material on roads or other common facilities, due to the movements of contaminated people, vehicles and things'. Over 90% of outbreaks in Cumbria fell into this category (Table 4).

Table 4. Percentage of spread of FMD infection between farms accounted for by specific routes of transfer for Cumbria and for other counties of England[43].

Routes of transfer	Cumbria (%)	Other counties (%)
Airborne	0.2	2.0
Milk tanker	0.8	0.6
Infected animals	4.0	6.3
Persons	2.3	6.2
Swill	0	0.1
Vehicle	1.0	2.3
Other carrier	0.3	1.1
Local transfer	91.4	81.4

We were informed that immediately FMD was discovered to have been at Longtown, the Market provided a full list of contacts to MAFF, including details of sheep purchasers on 15 February and 22 February and of market staff who worked or lived on agricultural holdings[44]. However, of the 36 part-time personnel, in this category, 34 had still not been contacted 6 weeks later. Similarly one of the buyers who had taken stock to Derbyshire was not contacted for 18 weeks. Copies of the Market's records were requested by MAFF a month after they were first supplied, as the originals had apparently been lost.

There has been Government speculation that 'trading outside the ring' may have created problems of unrecorded movements of sheep from markets. We cannot comment on the situation generally throughout Britain, but we are of the view that this was not a major issue at Longtown Market. There, animals are counted in and counted out of the Market both to ensure accountability of stock and to safeguard the Market's commission on the animals that are sold. It is in the Market's financial interest to ensure that selling outside the ring does not occur.

BIOSECURITY

Biosecurity was raised with us in a number of contexts. Based on what we learned during the Inquiry, the FMD movement restrictions on animals and people in Cumbria had been fully implemented and observed. Indeed, through a combination of closures of rights of way, decisions of visitors to keep away and a self-imposed 'battening down the hatches' by the whole community, the movement of people was curtailed beyond what might be argued as necessary. Very many businesses, organisations and individuals also introduced some form of biosecurity based on disinfectant footbaths or mats, usually at the gate or entrance to their property.

There was an equivocal view from both farmers and the public about the placing of disinfectant mats on public roadways; the consensus seemed to be that 'they did no harm and possibly some good'. Evidence from the Bewcastle Parish Council, whose area had escaped FMD although surrounded by outbreaks, expressed a conviction that road mats were very important as part of a defence strategy; others we spoke to were less convinced.

The Cumbria County Council deployed limited numbers of disinfectant mats and positioned them in strategic locations[45]. The policy that emerged was to place mats at the outer edges of the main outbreaks and try to isolate by road any individual outbreaks. In the later part of the epidemic mats were removed from the North and West of the County and concentrated around the 'Penrith Spur'. The Highways Agency, which is responsible for motorways and trunk roads, did not favour the use of mats because of the dangers to high volumes of fast moving traffic. There was some criticism of the Local Authorities policies on mats, but views were divided between those who would have been keen to see more in their own area of the County and those who were unconvinced of the benefits.

Some businesses and individuals also laid disinfectant road mats, but we learned of cases where different people laid acid and alkali mats at closely adjacent locations, creating an opportunity for the carriage of chemical from one to neutralised the other. Although either acid solutions (low pH) or alkali solutions (high pH) will deactivate the virus, where mats are used there is need for some co-ordination to avoid cross contamination.

The Northumberland Committee[46] was of the opinion that disinfectant mats on public roads are not effective in preventing the spread of foot and mouth disease and DEFRA has recently concurred, saying that it did not advocate mats but did give advice to those who wished to use them. We learned during the Inquiry that DEFRA advice to the County Council was contradictory, different guidance being provided on different occasions[47].

Footbaths were widely deployed, both where they were required by the FMD regulations and as a general precaution against the spread of the disease. These seemed generally to have been well maintained, although there was a criticism that some on public footpaths were possibly of inadequate concentration. There were also comments that whilst Government compensation was available for animals slaughtered under the FMD controls there was no assistance with the cost of preventative measures such as disinfectants.

We were particularly impressed by the way that the agricultural supply industries and milk collection services had moved quickly to introduce effective biosecurity measures, and to reduce traffic movements in and around infected areas[48]. We have already referred to the problem, early in the epidemic, of MAFF not making public the details of the exact farm locations of outbreaks. This created difficulties for the supply industries; we believe this policy was misjudged but assume that it will not be re-instituted in any future outbreak. Many businesses have carried some measure of increased biosecurity forward into their post-FMD operations. For example, on our visit to the Longtown Market we found the biosecurity measures to be extensive, and rigorously enforced. We noted that haulage contractors and milk collection services had reduced their level of biosecurity post-FMD.

One generic area of concern was the methods adopted for the cleaning of vehicles. We have noted that in some continental countries there is a recommendation against the use of pressure washers, on the basis that FMD virus in aerosol increases the risk of spread: low pressure washing or wiping down is favoured as an alternative. We have not encountered specific scientific data to allow us to draw firm conclusions on the best method for cleaning vehicles and we consider that the question needs to be researched.

There was also some debate about the best chemicals to use as disinfectants, although people in the agricultural industry had generally followed the approved list provided by DEFRA. From our own scientific understanding, there is evidence that the disassembly of the FMD virus at pH 6 or below takes place with the release of a specific protein fraction and viral RNA[49]. Also, during infection, viral RNA requires calcium ions to promote its entry into animal cells. Thus it can be reasoned that citrate buffers will be effective in deactivating the virus through effects on pH and calcium availability. Citrate buffers at pH 6 or less are safe and easy to handle and should markedly reduce any viral contamination on boots, and surfaces of vehicles, implements or buildings.

The most frequent biosecurity concerns raised with us related to the disease control operations themselves. There were three main concerns:

- that the movement of disease control staff between farms whilst making surveillance inspections or undertaking eradication operations had increased the risk (and the actuality) of disease spread;
- that the time taken for the slaughter and (separately) the disposal of stock had been over-long and increased risk of virus transfer via vermin or birds;
- that transport of carcasses for disposal or the airborne carriage of particles from pyres had increased disease spread.

We have discussed animal slaughter and disposal as topics in their own right in later paragraphs. With regard to disease control staff, we gained the impression that the majority of those involved adopted the biosecurity procedures recommended. However, farmers and others told us of individual instances where the biosecurity procedures adopted fell short of best practice, and were less rigorous than those being followed by farmers themselves. We have no basis for quantifying the scale of this problem but record that lapses in biosecurity did occur, and in some cases these reduced the farmers' confidence in the disease control staff.

We are also uneasy about the number of surveillance visits that were being made to some farms. We have no direct evidence that disease spread was increased. However, zone inspection procedures under *Form D* in areas suffering multiple FMD outbreaks created a surveillance regime that seems adverse to the creation of biosecurity cordons around uninfected premises. We learned of one farmer who had received 42 veterinary visits as a result of continually falling within *Form D* restrictions created by nearby infected premises; another farmer told us he had received 27 veterinary inspections[50].

Animal Slaughter

3KM CULL AND CONTIGUOUS CULL

The 3km cull and contiguous cull were very contentious - even amongst those farmers who were broadly in support. The Government's announcement of the 3km cull was poorly handled and, as initially made, was in error. In some instances of which we were appraised, the letter informing individual farmers of the decision to slaughter their sheep failed to provide a satisfactory explanation for the action being proposed. There was confusion amongst farmers about whether the slaughter was voluntary or mandatory, and an understandable perception that the authorities were acting threateningly. The way that some of these farmers were dealt with was heavy handed; it has left a legacy of damage to their respect for the authorities.

The quantitative scientific justification for the 3km cull has never been fully set out, and we learned in evidence that many vets in the field were strongly opposed to the idea. Our conjecture is that, when the policy was devised, there was a fear that FMD was out of control in Cumbria; that there was a danger of FMD becoming almost endemic in sheep in parts of the County. Moreover, increasing numbers of sheep were becoming 'trapped' on 'islands of land' because of the *Form D* movement restrictions; welfare problems were an increasing concern. Thus there seems to have been a decision to 'get ahead of the disease' and a pragmatic approach was adopted. This interpretation is consistent with the Minister of Agriculture's announcements in Parliament on 15 and 27 March, and with the advice of the EU Food and Veterinary Office mission to the Britain during 12-16 March[51].

The development of the contiguous culling policy was more scientific than the 3km cull, although it has proved equally contentious. The policy was based on a computer model providing a simulation of the epidemic. There has been scientific debate about the modelling approach and the validity of the assumptions about disease transmission. We have concluded that a scientific discussion of modelling is outwith the scope of this report and has been provided by the Royal Society.

For the present purpose, we would make two points. Firstly, the construction of robust computer models depends on sound scientific understanding of the system being modelled, and there are a number of uncertainties about the routes of local transmission of FMD in sheep. Secondly, endorsement of a model on the basis that the epidemic curves it produces are similar to those recorded in practice can be misleading. Correspondence of curves demonstrates only that the combination of assumptions in the model mathematically provides the same numerical outcome as the (possibly different) factors influencing the disease spread in the epidemic.

In the context of the Cumbria epidemic, the detail of the model underlying the contiguous culling policy could be regarded as somewhat academic. A 3km cull of sheep was already taking place, so the effect of the contiguous cull was to expand the slaughter to cattle on contiguous farms. It seems highly likely that this was one of the pragmatic options that had been considered earlier, before the modelling studies had taken place, and certainly it could be seen as consistent with the EU Food and Veterinary Office recommendation arising from its mission during 12-16 March.

TIME TO SLAUGHTER

Rapidity of slaughter of all susceptible animals at infected premises is a key feature in limiting FMD spread. The objective is to remove all sources of the virus by destroying both infected animals and any that could potentially be incubating or harbouring the virus; this can be perceived as 'over-kill' but the need is to destroy any potential sources of virus rather than just infected animals.

At the start of the epidemic veterinary instructions were that clinically infected animals should be slaughtered immediately and that others should be slaughtered 'with all practical speed'. In practice, however, the procedures from report to slaughter produced almost inevitable delay. We were told of the difficulties in farmers and veterinary practices getting telephone access to Rosehill. We learned of the frustrations of vets on the ground needing to have their diagnosis and actions confirmed from Page Street. DEFRA itself has cited the time needed to obtain stock valuations as a problem. These issues were progressively addressed but in our view they undoubtedly lengthened the time from first report to slaughter in the early stages of the epidemic. In regard to the need for confirmation by Page Street we note that the DEFRA is of the opinion that it did not cause delays[52]. We can only emphasise that DEFRA's view does not concur with the evidence we were given.

From 26 March DCCs were given more specific targets. Infected premises were to be slaughtered out within 24 hours of farmers' reports and contiguous premises within 48 hours (instructions for other dangerous contacts remaining unchanged). Analyses of the national DEFRA statistics by the Comptroller and Auditor General show that the setting of targets considerably shortened the 'time to slaughter' (Table 5). Nevertheless, even during the later stages of the epidemic, only slightly over half infected premises were slaughtered out within the 24-hour target.

Table 5. National time to slaughter statistics: percentage of premises slaughtered out in the time period indicated for infected premises, contiguous premises and other dangerous contacts. (Figures are rounded to the nearest percent.)

Infected premises	< 24 hours	24 – 36 hours	36 – 48 hours	> 48 hours
Pre 27 March	14	24	10	52
Post 27 March	51	35	4	10
Overall	41	32	6	22

Contiguous premises	< 24 hours	24 - 48 hours	48 - 72 hours	> 72 hours
Pre 27 March	1	5	6	88
Post 27 March	11	34	18	37
Overall	9	30	17	44

Other dangerous contact premises	< 24 hours	24 - 48 hours	48 - 72 hours	> 72 hours
Pre 27 March	5	10	10	75
Post 27 March	10	18	12	60
Overall	9	15	11	65

There were also significant differences in time to slaughter from one part of the country to another. The percentage of outbreaks slaughtered out in less than 24 hours, calculated for the whole of the epidemic, ranged from 0-60% between the 18 DCCs. Figures for the DCCs that handled the largest number of outbreaks (Table 6) show a range from 20-57 %, with the DCC for Cumbria in the middle of the range.

During the Inquiry we were provided with output sheets from a survey conducted by David Maclean MP over the period up to the end of April. These contained responses from farmers to a range of questions and included a question on the time between the report of FMD and their animals being slaughtered. This was not a statistically designed survey and lacked the rigorous records of an official system[53]. However, the 180 records showed that the time from initial 'report' to slaughter was: a day or less in 60% of cases; 1-2 days in 22% cases; 2-3 days in 8% cases; and longer than 3 days in 9% of cases. At the most extreme there were 4 cases where animals were reported to have been slaughtered 9-11 days after the initial report.

We received a wide range of comments about how the on-farm slaughter of animals was handled. In some cases there was very considerable appreciation of the sympathetic and understanding way that vets and slaughter teams had treated the farmers concerned. In other cases the reports were much less complementary. There were also accounts of slaughter teams turning up at the wrong farms and of 3km-zone farms that had not been slaughtered out although corresponding farms in the area had been.

For most farming families the on-farm slaughter of stock was a deeply traumatic process – an experience none will forget and many will take a long time to get over. Nonetheless, for commercial farmers and others, whose premises became infected, the slaughter was generally accepted as a necessary part of FMD eradication. It was much more difficult for those who had to endure the slaughter of apparently healthy stock as part of the 3km cull or contiguous cull. Amongst these families, there are cases of deep, and continuing, distress and resentment over the way that the policies were implemented.

Table 6. Percentage of infected premises slaughtered in less than 24 hours of report and percentage having animals disposed of in less than 24 hours of slaughter for the 6 Disease Control Centre areas in which there were more than 100 FMD outbreaks.

Disease Control Centre	Outbreaks	Duration of disease (days)	Slaughtered in < 24 hours of report (%)	Disposed of in < 24 hours of slaughter (%)
Carlisle	891	214	33	38
Newcastle	190	218	20	53
Dumfries and Galloway	177	83	27	51
Exeter	172	112	26	9
Leeds	140	164	57	77
Cardiff	101	165	37	65

The slaughter of animals is legally regulated[54], and these regulations applied during animal slaughter both on farm and at mass-slaughter sites. Notwithstanding this, we received a number of well-documented submissions referring to illegal slaughtering or alleged animal abuses at the time of slaughter[55]. Whilst most of the cases referred to could not be confirmed independently, we found the evidence that there had been instances of transgression to be convincing.

During the epidemic the RSPCA and the Humane Slaughter Association attended some culls and the RSPCA has been reported as having 'grave concern' at the level of veterinary supervision as a result of DEFRA resources being stretched. The RSPCA and Compassion in World Farming have apparently received many complains, from different parts of the country, about improper slaughtering; and the RSPCA has investigated over 90, 20 in detail. In many circumstances they have found good circumstantial evidence that an offence had been committed but, without the physical evidence of the carcasses, have decided that prosecution would be fruitless[56].

Whilst we reluctantly accept the difficulties of addressing what took place, we take the view that the application of any animal disease regulations must seek to maintain the highest standards of animal welfare and we are concerned to find that acceptably high standards were not always achieved.

Disposal and Cleansing

TIME TO DISPOSAL

Given the scale of the epidemic in Cumbria, disposal of animals from infected premises would always have provided a considerable challenge. But, in late March the challenge was increased because of the numbers of animals produced by the 3km cull and subsequently the contiguous cull. Overall the scale and logistics of the disposal task were immense.

During the first seven weeks of the epidemic, up to the third week in April, disposal nationally was lagging behind the slaughtering rate and there was a considerable build up of carcasses on farms. Thereafter, and with the deployment of troops, the speed of disposal became faster and the backlog on farms was progressively cleared. At the height of he epidemic approximate 54% of disposal was taking over 72 hours, 14% between 48 and 72 hours, 15% between 24 and 48 hours, and only 17% under 24 hours. However, by the beginning of May the under 24 hour figure had increased to approximately 88%. Over the whole of the epidemic the less than 24 hour disposal rate for the 6 most affected FMD areas (Table 6 above) ranged from 9 to 77% with the Cumbria being next to bottom at 38%.

We have also used the information from the 'Maclean survey' as a broad indicator of what was experienced locally, during the earlier part of the epidemic. The figures suggest that only about 20% of farms were experiencing slaughter to disposal times of less than 2 days. Corresponding percentages for longer time periods were: 14% of farms 2-3 days; 29% of farms 4-5 days; 19% of farms 6-7 days; 10% of farms 8-9 days; and 7% of farms 10 days or more[57]. In other words, it appears that on over a third of farms it was taking a week or more to dispose of slaughtered stock[58].

DISPOSAL POLICIES

Following the recommendations of the Northumberland Committee, the preferred method of carcass disposal at the start of the 2001 epidemic was burial on farm or failing that, burning. However, at an early stage of the epidemic (seemingly as something of a surprise) it was recognised that all on-farm burial sites would require authorisations from the Environment Agency to comply with the Groundwater Regulations (1998) and would also need to comply with the Animal Waste Directive.

By 6 March, discussions with the Environment Agency resulted in an agreed hierarchy of disposal which placed rendering and incineration first, followed by licensed commercial landfill and mass burial; on-farm burial and burning were placed low in the hierarchy because of concerns over their impact on the environment. During March and April there were further discussions between DEFRA and the Environment Agency, and advice from the Department of Health (DoH) and the Spongiform Encephalopathy Advisory Committee (SEAC). By late April the preferred hierarchy was as shown in Table 7. Thus during the course of the epidemic the underlying policies in regard to disposal changed, although in parts of the country the impact of this was constrained because of the limited availability of some of the preferred options. In describing the evolving policies the Government has identified three main phases.

Phase 1 (from 20 February) was carried out in accordance with pre-existing veterinary guidelines based on open pyres or on-farm burial where ground water approvals could be obtained. At the same time systems were developed for the sealed-lorry transport of carcasses to biosecure rendering plants and 6 plants were progressively brought into operation; incinerators were fully committed to dealing with animals and specified risk tissues deriving from the BSE control programmes. Mass burn sites, where FMD animals from several farms could be brought together, were also established but were highly contentious. This led to the mass burial sites being identified, including Watchtree near Great Orton.

Phase 2 (from 20 March) saw the mass burial sites being brought fully into operation, and some use of landfill sites for the disposal of animals slaughtered under the Livestock Welfare (Disposal) Scheme and the Light Lamb Scheme. There was also a more rigorous separation protocol for cattle over 5-years old, in accord with SEAC's advice. The use of air curtain burners imported from the USA was also piloted in some areas. Two such burners were brought to Cumbria and stored at Great Orton but were not brought into use because other disposal options were available[59].

Table 7. Approved hierarchy of disposal routes for different species and age of stock.

Preferred method of disposal	Permitted animals
1. Rendering.	All.
2. High-temperature incineration.	All.
3. Landfill on approved sites.	Sheep, pigs of any age and cattle born after 1 August 1996.
4. Burning.	All (with limits of 1,000 cattle per pyre).
5. Mass burial or on farm burial on approved sites.	Sheep and pigs of any age and cattle born after 1 August 1996.

Phase 3 (from 20 April) developed as the disposal procedures caught up with the rate of slaughter. The rendering plant capacity was then more able to cope and by early May the use of pyres was discontinued throughout England and Wales. At the same time the Watchtree disposal site was closed for reception of carcasses (although still in operation dealing with leachate removal and environmental restoration).

DISPOSAL ISSUES

Carcass disposal was one of the most multi-dimensional topics falling within the Inquiry's remit. It had important economic, social and health aspects, which are considered in Part 3 of this report, and aspects related to FMD control which we have summarised here.

Biosecurity

There appears to be a well-established view that the rapid disposal of carcasses plays an almost insignificant part in FMD control. It is succinctly summarised by the Comptroller and Auditor General who writes:

'*Rapid disposal of carcasses is not critical to disease control, unless it holds up slaughter. The risk of disease transmission is low, as the virus is not produced after the animal is killed. The risk is reduced by regular disinfecting and by PVC covering of the heads and feet of infected animals and the restrictions in place at infected premises. After 30 days or so natural decomposition destroys the virus. However, carcasses awaiting disposal are at risk from scavengers which theoretically may spread the disease, though during this outbreak no spread by this route has been confirmed*'.

We are happy to accept that the risk of FMD spread is hugely reduced by slaughter, especially in pigs and cattle where the exhalation of virus is very high. However, we are less sanguine that there is a full understanding of the risk associated with infected carcasses lying in the open for long periods, as occurred in Cumbria during the 2001 epidemic. A number of witnesses have provided evidence (including photographs and video recordings) of slaughtered sheep, lying uncovered immediately adjacent to public roadways[60]. They have also described and photographed what appears to be effluent and seepage from the carcasses 'pooling' nearby. Under these circumstances, the risk of spread by vermin, birds or passing traffic seems likely to be increased above the 'theoretical'. This is of concern, particularly since a very high proportion of disease spread in the recent epidemic was attributed to poorly characterised routes of 'local spread'.

We were also told that effluent loss had been observed from the lorries carrying carcasses from farms for burial or incineration sites[61]. Concerns were also expressed that lorries varied their routes, increasing risk of the potential spread of effluent over a wide area. We noted that DEFRA had developed biosecurity protocols for loading and leak testing the disposal lorries but, on the basis of what we have learned, biosecurity in practice was not foolproof. Any attendant risk will clearly depend on the potential virus load in the carcass effluent, which relates back to our concerns in the previous paragraph.

Risk Analysis

In considering the factors that had influenced the choices of disposal methods (both in Cumbria and nationally) we became conscious of the complexities arising as a result of the range of public agencies involved. For example, whilst the Environment Agency is responsible for environmental aspects of burial, such as ground water contamination, it is not responsible for air quality, except in the case of factory emissions. Air quality related to pyres falls mainly to the local Environmental Health Department or the local Public Health Department or DoH (nationally). DEFRA has responsibilities for the safe disposal of FMD carcasses under the relevant FMD legislation, but its responsibility relates primarily to animal health. In matters related to food the Food Standards Agency (FSA) has a role, either directly or through its advisory committees such as SEAC. Given these arrangements we became concerned that there was more than a possibility that every agency might act to minimise its own risk and that consideration of the aggregate consequences of different disposal options could suffer.

We received several expressions of concern about the potential risk of FMD spread from pyres. There is no doubt that well managed burning destroys most pathogens and we understand that a correctly built pyre should have burned out in about 3-4 days. In Cumbria, pyres often burned or smouldered for several weeks[62] which implies that they were either built incorrectly or that the materials used were unfit for the purpose. We were told that in some cases there was deposition of fragments of what appeared to be carcass material at considerable distances from the pyres[63]. We noted that this was not a topic on which DEFRA published its risk assessment, to have done so might have reassured farmers and the public.

CLEANSING

We received a range of comments about the cleansing operations. In some cases the cleansing teams were regarded to have moved in quickly and undertaken their work efficiency. In other cases farmers had experienced problems. Criticisms, where they occurred, were various: the work had not been completed with much urgency and had offered poor value for public expenditure; parts of the work undertaken had been over-specified or were considered to be more than required; personnel were poorly trained or lacked experience. There were also significant differences in the procedures that were required in different areas (both within and outwith Cumbria). This led to the impression that there was no clear scientific and technical consensus about what was required, and that there was a lack of clear guidance within DEFRA.

There were two points that we noted particularly. Firstly, some grievances had much to do with the bureaucracy and inflexibility of DEFRA's administrative procedures. Secondly, there were still unresolved disputes over payments for work that was claimed to have been undertaken by farmers 'under instruction from DEFRA' (not always with written confirmation).

Effectiveness of Disease Control

The epidemic in Cumbria was the largest and the second most persistent in Britain. And, from our public meetings, we became aware of an underlying suspicion that the disease had been less effectively controlled in Cumbria than elsewhere. We sought to test this hypothesis, although we are first to acknowledge the limitations of the comparisons than can be made.

Overall, our conclusion is that Cumbria experienced a similar level of disease control to the average of the remainder of Britain and that the size of the epidemic was largely due to the scale of the initial level of infection. This reasoning takes account of three points. Firstly, given the ratio of the published estimates of the number of outbreaks seeded across Britain at the start of the outbreak (57) and the total number of outbreaks recorded (2,026), there is nothing inconsistent about the scale of the Cumbria epidemic. In proportion to the number of seeded outbreaks (38) the number of total outbreaks (893) is well within the range that might be anticipated. Secondly, although the time to slaughter statistics for Cumbria could be regarded as less than satisfactory, there is no indication of any systematic association between the slaughter and disposal statistics and the size or duration of particular regional epidemics (see Table 6). Finally, within the limits of comparison the epidemic curve for Cumbria was similar to the epidemic curve for the remainder of the country (Figure 3).

Figure 3. Number of outbreaks for the week commencing the indicated date for Cumbria and for the rest of the UK.

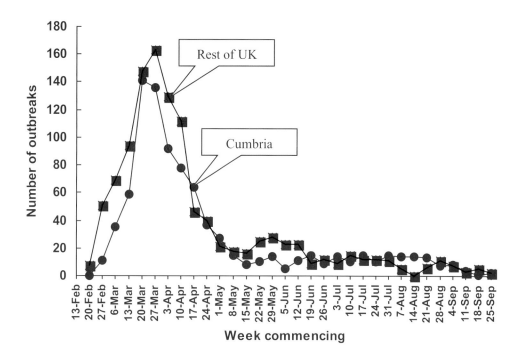

Consistent with the introduction of the 3km cull (after 15 March), the Cumbria outbreaks began to decline ahead the national trend. However, there seems to have been no change in rate of decline after the additional introduction of the contiguous cull (after 26 March). There is a suggestion that, from the peak of the epidemic, the rate of decline may have been slightly slower in Cumbria, but both there and elsewhere the epidemic had reduced to the 'tail' levels by the week commencing 8 May.

We have also asked ourselves how the management of the epidemic in Cumbria compared with the management of epidemics in other specific locations. Here we had particularly noted the large differences in duration of the epidemics in different parts of the country, and the short duration of the Dumfries and Galloway epidemic. Any analysis of the data must be made with reservations because the epidemics were of a different scale in terms of numbers of cases. However, taking the six areas shown in Table 6, the evidence seems to suggest that the duration of the epidemic was reduced as the ratio of 'exposed' premises culled to infected premises culled increased (Figure 4). The higher ratios indicate a more rigorous culling policy with regard to 3km-zone premises and contiguous premises as well the tracing and rigorous elimination of dangerous contacts.

Figure 4. The relationship between the duration of FMD epidemics in different parts of the country in days and the ratio of number of 'exposed' contiguous and other premises culled to number of infected premises culled. (Data[64] is for the six areas of epidemic indicated in Table 6).

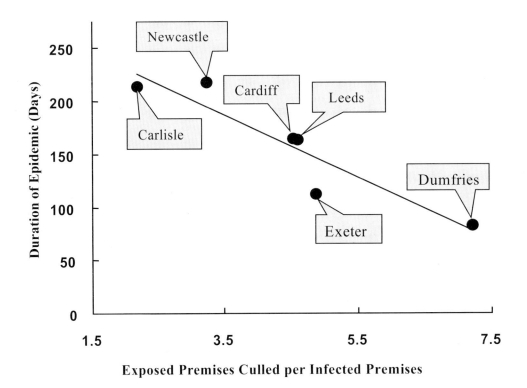

Other Issues

MEAT IMPORTS

Amongst both farmers and other members of the public, opinion was strongly in favour of more rigorous and effective controls on the importation of meat to Britain. There was a full understanding that the disease had originated from outside the country and, whilst there were some voices of concern about 'modern farming methods', better regulation of importation was seen as essential. There was a strong view that Government was not moving quickly enough to strengthen import inspections and controls.

DEFRA told us that since the end of FMD the Government had made a number of changes to reduce the risk from imports and listed actions taken as follows:

- increased enforcement powers to allow inspectors to take action at retail points and to search commercial consignments and personal luggage;
- increased public awareness through information for travellers, including information at Embassies, on websites and on posters;
- improved intelligence gathering and sharing of information by enforcement agencies, including establishing a central database of information;
- meeting and listening to the concerns and ideas of agencies, leaders of farming, food, rural, environmental and consumer interests and producing an action plan[65];
- carrying out risk assessment and providing information to assist enforcement authorities to target their operations against illegal imports;
- funding a new unit within DEFRA to take forward the action in close co-operation with others;
- plans further to improve risk assessment, pilots in the use of detector dogs and to tighten UK and EU rules and deterrents on illegal imports.

The recent publication of a new guide to import controls and the public announcement of new Government initiatives[66] should also be noted.

LESSONS FROM 1967-68

There was a public perception that in its policies and actions in dealing with FMD the Government had failed to take account of the lessons learned from previous epidemics, specifically the Northumberland Committee Report on the 1967-68 epidemic. Some comments were directed at the rejection of on-farm burial as a preferred method of carcass disposal, which we have dealt with earlier.

More broadly our finding was that the recommendations of the Northumberland Committee Report were generally followed. DEFRA has reported that, of the 112 recommendations, 89 were applied fully, 15 were applied in part but modified to the 2001 conditions, 6 were not relevant in 2001, and 2 were rejected[67]. However, perhaps the most important recommendation of Northumberland was the emphasis on rapid culling and disposal of animals as soon as FMD had been diagnosed. The evidence suggests that in Cumbria in 2001 sufficient speed of action in culling and disposing may not have been achieved. We are therefore concerned that DEFRA has seemingly reverted to its view that the role of the CVO in confirming FMD remains paramount. We believe that in the early stages of the 2001 epidemic this led to unnecessary delay, which should be avoided in any future outbreak.

ANIMALS SLAUGHTERED

FMD in sheep can be difficult to diagnose, and we received a number of reports of the problems encountered amongst temporary vets from overseas, a proportion of whom were unfamiliar with common UK sheep diseases. A few farmers expressed concern that some positive cases of FMD might have been misdiagnosed. National statistics for laboratory confirmation of FMD diagnosis have now been published. These indicate that 90% of diagnosed FMD cases were submitted for laboratory confirmation, and that of these 78% tested positive and 22% tested negative. We were advised that the percentage of animals testing positive in Cumbria was above the national average. As would be expected, the indicative rate of positive laboratory confirmation of FMD in animals slaughtered on contiguous premises was much lower at 30%, and even this figure is likely to be an overestimate[68].

A number of people also drew attention to the relatively large number of animals that were slaughtered, particularly in comparison to 1967-68. The raw figures suggest that the number of animals slaughtered in 2001 was about 9.5 times that in 1967-68, but that figure is misleading for a number of reasons. The factor that determines whether animals are culled is the premises they are on; thus the number of animals per hectare and the size of farms will influence the number of animals slaughtered. In 2001, FMD was mainly in sheep rather than cattle and farms were generally larger. Taking these factors into account the 2001 slaughter may have been nearer to twice that in 1967-68 on a 'comparable basis'.

However, there is little doubt that a large number of uninfected sheep were slaughtered as a result of the 3km-zone and contiguous culling policies. We were told that of a sample of almost 5,800 sheep tested at the Watchtree mass burial site only a handful was positive for FMD[69]. However, interpretation of that statistic depends on whether the 3km-zone and contiguous culls are considered as a policy to remove potentially 'at risk' animals or as a policy to remove animals that were already infected.

VACCINATION

Opinions on vaccination were divided, even amongst the vets and farmers who presented evidence or attended our meetings. There was a consensus that vaccination has a role to play, and that it should be considered in planning any future disease control strategy. However, there were mixed views about whether vaccination should have been deployed in 2001 and about how it might best be used at some stage in the future.

Under the present EU policies, embodied in Directives 85/51/EEC and 90/423/EEC, vaccination against FMD is not permitted except as an 'emergency vaccination' to deal with a FMD outbreak. In this context in can be applied in two ways: 'protective', where the animals are allowed to live out their economic lives (sometimes referred to as vaccinate-to-live); and 'suppressive' where the animals are subsequently destroyed as part of the 'stamping out' policy. Suppressive vaccination can be used strategically to check the spread of FMD and gain time for the orderly slaughter and disposal of animals; it includes 'ring vaccination', in which the locus of the outbreak is surrounded, or 'firebreak' or 'buffer zone' vaccination.

From the start of the 2001 FMD outbreak vaccination was an option, and in late March and early April the Government considered it specifically as a strategy for dealing with the epidemic in Cumbria. Ring vaccination was ruled out because the epidemic was regarded to have spread too widely; but on 28 March EU authorisation was secured for protective vaccination of cattle. The underlying reasoning was that the area was considered so heavily infected with FMD that cattle would be at high risk as soon as they were turned out from their winter quarters. Vaccination would therefore prevent an explosion of cattle FMD and attendant logistical problems of slaughter and disposal.

However, creation of a protective vaccination zone would have had significant regulatory[70] and market consequences for both the beef and dairy sectors. Meat from vaccinated animals slaughtered for consumption within 30 days of vaccination would have had to be heat-treated. Thereafter, for a period of 12 months from vaccination or from the last confirmed FMD case in the zone, it would have had to be deboned and matured for 24 hours before entering the food chain. Correspondingly, for a period of 12 months from vaccination, milk would have had to be pasteurised[71], and for the first 30 days that pasteurisation would have had to take place within the vaccination zone[72]. Vaccinated animals would not have been allowed to move out of the zone for 12 months, except under licence to slaughter, and the taking of semen or ova from vaccinated cattle would have been prohibited.

The practical consequences of these conditions were deeply worrying for farmers and the food trade. Firstly there was every indication that there would be no realistic markets for heat-treated beef or, with the added costs, for the deboned matured product. Secondly, there was insufficient milk processing capacity solely in Cumbria to take all the milk being produced there. Finally, the sole Cumbrian processor, Nestle, expressed serious reservations about accepting the milk from vaccinated cows because of a perceived adverse consumer reaction, particularly in overseas markets. With farmers reluctant to agree to vaccination until they could gain some reassurance from Government about the implications for farm produce, the 'Nestle factor' appears to have been crucial. With the number of FMD outbreaks beginning to reduce sharply vaccination of cattle was shelved.

Several people with whom we discussed the vaccination issue took a general view that prophylactic vaccination against FMD would be the ideal prevention strategy[73]. However, for a country such as Britain, which imports food from all over the world, the serotype specificity of the present generation of vaccines is a significant limitation. Those who argue in favour of general vaccination rightly point out that the National and World FMD Reference Centre, Pirbright, monitors FMD outbreaks internationally. A vaccination strategy could therefore be based on the serotype of greatest perceived risk to the UK. However, this would provide no guarantee of protection since illegal imports of food (and different serotypes) could come from almost anywhere in the world. The development of improved vaccines with a broader specificity appears to scientifically feasible, and as they become available the dilemma of vaccine selection will be resolved[74].

However, significant trade and market issues would still need to be addressed. These are also a consideration if zoned or more widespread vaccination is undertaken after an outbreak has occurred and the FMD virus has been typed. Antibody tests able to distinguish animals with FMD virus antibodies from those that have been vaccination with modern vaccines against the virus are now available. These provide a potential means of meeting the OIE requirements for demonstrating a 'virus-free vaccinated-zone' status, although they have yet to be adopted as an approach within the EU. Thus, for the present, it appears that the main questions to be addressed are whether, within the limits of current vaccine technology and accepted testing regimes, vaccination should be used in an FMD outbreak, and if so how. We have considered this in our conclusions and recommendations.

In Cumbria there is a special consideration of the protection of heafed sheep, particularly of the Herdwick, Rough Fell and Swaledale breeds, which have a significant rural heritage value. The case has been made to us that such animals should be protected by vaccination if there is any future FMD outbreak in the region. Whilst we have empathy with the sentiment that the heafed sheep are of special significance, we find it difficult to construct a sustainable case for specific breeds, or groups of animals, being treated as an exception, so long as they are being farmed commercially and entering the food chain. Any practical strategy for dealing with FMD control in livestock entering the food chain would need to be area based and cover all susceptible livestock.

Conclusions and Recommendations

Planning, Resources and Management

Even making full allowances for the almost unique circumstances that arose during the 2001 FMD epidemic in Cumbria, we were disturbed by the range of systems failings identified during this part of the Inquiry. Many of the points we have highlighted below relate to MAFF/DEFRA, but the challenge of achieving effective two-way communications between communities in the regions and central government has implications far wider than our present remit in respect of FMD.

A lack of appropriate contingency planning and a failure to adhere to some of the provisions in the contingency plan that existed compromised the FMD disease control campaign from the outset. This was made worse by the insularity of the local Animal Health Office and a failure to adopt a multi-agency approach in shaping its early response to the disease. Things did improve in later March but the measures effected then should have been in place sooner.

DEFRA has now published an updated draft Contingency Plan, which has been put out for consultation. We have concluded the plan requires very substantial revision. We have also concluded that as a matter of fundamental policy it should be revised as a multi-agency plan, engaging all the relevant agencies, including the Local Authorities. It is no longer sensible to consider FMD wholly in isolation from other areas of emergency planning. The devastation the disease can bring is now fully apparent, and after 11 September 2001 bio-terrorism must be regarded as an additional risk factor.

We accept the rationale of the decision made by Cumbria County Council to await a lead from MAFF/DEFRA, and not to open the County's Emergency Centre. However, we believe that in planning for a future multi-agency response the Emergency Centre should be considered as a 'hub' facility[75]. This should be agreed with DEFRA within the framework of contingency planning.

We recommend that DEFRA undertakes a comprehensive revision of its draft contingency plan in the light of the findings of this and other FMD Inquiries. The plan should be conceived on a multi-agency basis and should engage all the relevant agencies, including the County Councils. In local FMD planning, the Cumbria County Council Emergency Centre should be considered as a 'hub' facility for any future multi-agency response.

We can make no objective comment on the adequacy of the resources at the Carlisle Animal Health Office before the outbreak of FMD began, although we observed that the geographical area that was being covered from the Office intuitively seemed 'large'. There seems little doubt that as soon as FMD outbreaks began the Office was quickly overwhelmed. Whilst the number of personnel at the peak of the FMD operations was adequate to deal with the task, the rate at which additional manpower was brought to bear was too slow. There were also problems related to the limited training given to personnel and their lack of local knowledge. In Cumbria, if not elsewhere in Britain, the Army should have been brought in sooner.

It has been suggested that there was a shortage of vets to undertake surveillance and diagnostic work, and we encountered some evidence that this may have been the case in Cumbria. However, we also noted several comments from vets that their time should have been used more efficiently. The logistics of veterinary deployment and the automatic serving of a *Form A*, which demanded examinations of all the stock on a farm even on the report of a single sick animal showing symptoms unlikely to be FMD, were both subject to criticism.

We have no basis for judging the adequacy of the present level of staffing in the Carlisle Animal Health Office but we assume that DEFRA has considered it in relation to the envisaged workload. Clearly, it would be wholly inappropriate to base staffing on the levels needed during the FMD epidemic. However, personnel plans should be considered as part of the contingency planning process for any future outbreak of FMD. Whilst the need for appropriate numbers of veterinary staff has been recognised we also formed the view that there was an equivalent need for managers, administrators and logistics experts in the event of a FMD outbreak.

We recommend that DEFRA, in conjunction with partner organisations and veterinary practices throughout Cumbria, reviews personnel requirements (both numbers of personnel and provision of preparatory training) as part of its contingency planning process. Likewise, the local Contingency Plan should specify clearly the stage and scale of epidemic that will trigger a request from DEFRA for assistance from the Army.

Speed of response in halting animal movements and in making decisions to cull infected animals or dangerous contacts is crucial in getting on top of FMD, and the evidence suggests that in the early phase of the 2001 epidemic there were delays that should have been avoided. **We recommend that, in any future outbreak, movement restrictions are introduced as soon as the first case is diagnosed and that provisions are introduced to deal with animals in transit. Additionally, local authorisation of action in dealing with an outbreak should be introduced as early as possible, with DEFRA headquarters kept fully informed of decisions.**

DEFRA has now published on the Internet a range of very useful risk analysis documents covering various aspects of FMD and its control. **We recommend that DEFRA's risk analysis documents be reviewed from time to time and revised as necessary. A statement of the risk of spread of FMD (or other diseases) through the carriage of particulate matter from pyres should be added. Also, in conjunction with the other agencies with statutory, enforcement or health responsibilities, DEFRA should published a risk analysis of all the carcass disposal options, include computer modelling of the consequences of breakdown in biosecurity in any phase of the elected disposal strategies.**

As a result of the handling of FMD, the farming and rural communities of Cumbria have suffered an enormous loss in confidence in DEFRA. It will be an uphill struggle for the Department to restore the relationships that are necessary for its effective interface with its client groups. From what we have learned we can only conclude that DEFRA has significant problems of systems of operation and of staff training and development that should be addressed as a matter of urgency. It is also important for the future of the Department that it creates a 'new start' in its relationship with its client groups in Cumbria. Therefore **we recommend that as a matter of priority DEFRA resolves all outstanding disputes and settles all financial accounts relating to the FMD epidemic in Cumbria by 31 March 2003.**

Epidemiology

There is no way of being sure, but the evidence suggested that a failure to identify, destroy and dispose of dangerous contacts or exposed animals sufficiently quickly contributed to the duration and the scale of the Cumbria epidemic. That has led us to focus on the epidemiological studies that were undertaken as part of the ongoing disease control efforts and the later *post mortem* analysis of events.

There are indications that there were not enough personnel with epidemiological training to fulfil the requirements for pursuing dangerous contacts in the field. Similarly, in the light of so many farm cases being attributed to 'local transfer' we have concerns about whether the case control model adopted in the epidemiological work was sufficiently discriminatory to provide the information necessary to understand the transmission of disease and so develop improved methods of biosecurity. There is an urgent need for the epidemiological information from the 2001 epidemic to be analysed and published so that it can inform research into FMD and biosecurity.

We recommend that DEFRA commissions an external review of its provision of epidemiological support in connection with FMD, and of the usefulness of the data collected to the understanding of disease spread.

Biosecurity

Britain's front line of biosecurity is at the points of entry to the country from overseas. Thus controls on legal and illegal imports of meat are a key consideration in avoiding any future

FMD outbreak. We welcome the actions the Government has taken so far to improve import control. However, it is still difficult to have confidence that Britain's import control systems are sufficiently rigorous. **We recommend that the Government publish performance targets and annual performance statistics in respect of import controls in order to promote public confidence in the new measures that have been introduced.**

There is a case for improved training of farmers in biosecurity and disease recognition, and for the on-farm 'quarantining' of newly arrived animals to reduce risk of disease spread. Likewise the traceability of animals through the food chain is an accepted requirement of modern good practice. However, we believe that overburdening bureaucracy and unnecessary regulatory constraints should be guarded against, and that any measures that are introduced longer term should be clearly targeted. At present there seems to be some policy confusion between the target of increasing farm biosecurity and that of reducing rapid, long distance movements of livestock. It was the second that was largely responsible for the countrywide distribution of FMD virus in 2001.

We recommend that the current 'standstill' regulations continue to be reviewed to identify practical policies for increased biosecurity that will be more compatible with the needs of commercial farming systems. Through its agencies Government should ensure the provision of training courses for farmers on biosecurity and disease recognition.

There were several areas of biosecurity where we identified a need for better information and knowledge, based on research. These areas included: the disinfecting of vehicles; use of disinfectant road mats; and potential disease spread from effluent from carcasses lying in the open or in transit for disposal. In 2001 there was a lack of authoritative information and guidance on biosecurity from the government scientists, resulting in a great deal of public uncertainty and disruption to many public services.

We fully understand the arguments against the introduction of Government funding for disinfectant use on farms, but pragmatically, on the basis of value for public money, there is a justifiable case for the total public support measures being evaluated in the round. This argues for an economic appraisal of the financial benefit arising from the funding of disease prevention measures rather than simply disease control measures.

We recommend that DEFRA commissions research on biosecurity to provide a robust understanding of the biosecurity measures appropriate to safeguard against FMD spread. The cost benefit of public funding for preventative biosecurity measures in the event of a FMD outbreak should be examined.

Developing an Integrated Strategy

There is no doubt that Britain will have future challenges from the FMD virus. In thinking about this we have concluded that there is a need for an integrated strategy based on risk analysis to address the issues raised by the 2001 epidemic. This will require national and local initiatives and, as we have conceived it, might be integrated under the following five themes.

- Prevention
- Planning
- Prompt response
- Premeditated tactics
- Prepared recovery

Prevention would involve action to make sure that the biosecurity cordon created by Britain's island geography is effective against entry of disease from other countries. Risk analysis should be based on up-to-date intelligence on international disease outbreaks, and on legal and illegal movements of food and other agricultural produce. Risk management should be effected through tight regulatory controls and rigorous enforcement at all points of entry. Enforcement of food law through the Local Authorities should establish a priority for the identification and tracing of any illegally imported food products. EU and international agreements on the movement of foods should be reviewed in the light of identified biosecurity requirements. Allocation of manpower and other resources should be sufficient to achieve a radical reduction in the risk of FMD being introduced to Britain.

Planning should ensure that national and local Contingency Plans are realistic and comprehensive. They should be constructed on a multi-agency basis and should build on fully integrated risk analyses of all relevant procedures. Risk analysis studies should be made widely available and wherever possible should be published electronically. Plans should be tested by simulation exercises at local level at no more than 2-year intervals, and the analysis should be accessible to all partner agencies.

Prompt response would focus on early detection and prompt reaction once the disease has entered the country. It would include training and disease alert programmes for farmers and the use of biosecurity in providing within-country disease barriers. Prompt response would include isolation of premises, introduction of Restricted Infected Area provisions and a national restriction of livestock movements until the distribution of the disease could be assessed. Risk analysis would include assessment of alternative strategies and consequences of risk management breakdowns in any area of the response framework.

Prepared Tactics must take account of the fact that no two FMD outbreaks will be identical. Thus the most appropriate tactics for disease control and eradication will depend on the particular circumstances of the outbreak. The tactics to be adopted in different circumstances should nonetheless be planned on a scenario basis and published. This would allow agencies involved in disease control and businesses in the agricultural sector to be aware of the tactics that will be adopted in a particular type of disease outbreak. It would also take the scientific and technical issues related to the control and eradication of the disease out of the arena of political debate.

Decisions on optimum tactics would be greatly assisted by quick diagnostic field tests for FMD and by robust epidemiological models. These should be identified, agreed and introduced as a matter of urgency; where appropriate, limitations on the present understanding of the spread of disease should be factored into the risk analysis models. Quick diagnostic testing is a specific need since it is an essential component in tactical decision making.

Present 'gold standard' testing regimes based on virus isolation in tissue culture can take up to 4 days, and whilst ELISA (Enzyme-linked Immunosorbent Assay) tests for antigens can be undertaken in 4 hours, they are less reliable in sheep and goats than in pigs and cattle. New techniques based on RT-PCR (Reverse Transcriptase-Polymerase Chain Reaction) technology, which determine RNA at very low levels, have been under development. One such system being developed in the USA for on-farm diagnosis is claimed to detect all 7 serotypes of the FMD virus, and in a test time of less than 1 hour[76]. It will apparently also detect the FMD virus at the pre-clinical stage. A test of this type would offer very significant benefits in the control of the disease in practice.

Tactical approaches to FMD control and eradication should be based on the principle of a hierarchy of responses. This would work on agreed 'trigger points' which would determine the disease control actions to be taken in the particular circumstances. The detail of the hierarchy and the appropriate control tactics require examination beyond the remit of this report. However, the underlying concept is that different control actions are appropriate to deal with a single FMD outbreak or small confined cluster, or a larger zone of infection, or something approaching a pandemic, as occurred in Cumbria in 2001. In each case the risk arising from the application of a particular tactic requires to be assessed

With a single case or a small confined outbreak, a policy of rapid identification, slaughter and disposal of animals at infected premises and all dangerous contacts is probably the appropriate response. However, for a larger zone of outbreak vaccination becomes a tactical tool to be deployed at an early stage. In these circumstances ring vaccination followed by slaughter of animals within the ring (similar to the approach used in the Netherlands) may offer some advantages. It rapidly brings the spread of disease under control whilst allowing slaughter and disposal to be undertaken in a well-organised fashion. A variant of this approach might be to vaccinate, and then rapidly to test animals within the ring zone and to slaughter only where there is evidence of infection.

Where there is widespread infection or multiple clusters of infection, so that large numbers of animals are involved, vaccination must be regarded as an essential element in the control strategy. Under these circumstances there is a significant risk that slaughtering to 'stamp out' the disease will fail to keep up with its spread, and disposal will fail to keep up with slaughtering. In short, there is the risk of creating circumstances similar to those which occurred in Cumbria in 2001, where large-scale slaughter of animals was ineffective as a rapid and efficient method of disease control. We believe those circumstances should be avoided at all costs[77].

Additionally, under the circumstances of a large outbreak there is a justifiable case for a 'vaccinate-to-live' policy. However, this raises two associated issues. Firstly, any sub-division of the country so that a zone of vaccination could be declared, requires prior assessment of access to meat and milk processing plants; the borders of an appropriate vaccination zone may not correspond with county or other borders. Secondly, a vaccination-to-live policy would require a livestock support regime that would offset market failures occurring as a result of the vaccination policy adopted. However, we understand that such a scheme might be acceptable under EU law.

Prepared recovery would cover the aftermath and immediate recovery period after a FMD epidemic, and would involve planning rapidly to re-establish normal business and community activities in an affected area. This would form part of any normal 'corporate' crisis plan and equally should be a component in national planning. Such an approach would help to avoid the kind of hiatus in public policy decisions which has slowed aspects of industrial and rural recovery after the 2001 epidemic.

We recommend that Government establish an independent Working Party to develop an integrated risk-assessed strategy for defence against FMD, covering prevention of disease entry to the Britain, contingency planning, response to disease detection, tactics for disease control and eradication, and post-outbreak recovery.

PART 3: ECONOMIC, ENVIRONMENTAL AND SOCIAL IMPACTS

When FMD struck Cumbria it caused major economic, environmental and social impacts which were created in three main ways. Firstly, the disease had direct and indirect effects on farming and related industries. Secondly, the powerful message that people should 'stay off' farmland, together with the restrictions placed on access, affected tourism, outdoor leisure businesses and the outdoor amenity of local communities. Thirdly, the slaughter and, particularly, disposal of animals on pyres and in mass burial sites close to settlements transformed the Cumbrian environment, and with it the lives of the rural community. Combined together these events caused a huge level of trauma and distress for many in the population, and brought attendant concerns about short-term and long-term problems of health.

In Part 3 of our report we review the economic, environmental and social impacts of FMD disease on Cumbria but first, as necessary background, we have examined the impact of FMD on countryside access.

Countryside Access

In the evidence we received the 'closure of the countryside' due to FMD was widely regarded as one of the most damaging consequences of the epidemic. It was certainly one of the most divisive in setting one part of the community against another and all parts of the community against the authorities. Many businesses suffered deeply as a result in the drastic fall in visitors to Cumbria, and in their comments to us the most common questions were 'How and why did the closure of the countryside occur?' and 'Why did it go on for so long?'. We have therefore sought to understand what took place and to put the decisions and actions into context.

POLICY AND LEGISLATION

According to the Government's own account, its policy on access to the countryside seems to have gone through a cycle of change over the first month after FMD broke out. However, its initial response was very clear. As the degree of spread of the disease was unknown, the decision was made to advise the public to stay off farmland and avoid contact with farm animals. A news release conveying this message was made on 23 February 2001 and it was backed up with strong statements from the Agriculture Minister and the Prime Minister. The next day the whole of Britain was made a Controlled Area and bans on animal movements and on fairs, markets and field sports were introduced.

By 27 February, there were FMD cases in Essex, Northumberland, Devon and Anglesey and legislation was urgently approved giving Local Authorities new powers under the Foot and Mouth Disease Order, 1983. Up to that time certain powers under the legislation were held by the Minister of Agriculture, the CVO and Divisional Veterinary Officers but other powers were under the control of 'inspectors' appointed for the purpose by DEFRA or the Local Authorities[78]. Thus in these parts of the legislation there were dual controls, and one such part was the power to prohibit entry of persons to land or agricultural buildings in Infected Areas, notwithstanding the existence of a footpath or Right of Way

On 27 February the Local Authorities powers were expanded by two changes. Firstly, the powers of the 'inspector' under the dual role were increased so that access closures could be made in Controlled Areas, as distinct from Infected Areas (which are smaller). Secondly, the Local Authorities were given wholly new powers to close any land areas in which FMD was confirmed or (after consultation with DEFRA) any non-infected areas, closed in the interests of preventing the spread of FMD. Later, on 6 March, Government guidance was issued to the Local Authorities on their use of these powers, but by that time most rural Local Authorities had taken action to implement the legal powers that had been urgently allocated to them. Moreover, the only comment the guidance made on risk assessment was that access should be closed to land or premises where it would 'increase the risk of potential disease spread'.

Subsequently, however, the Government's policy was to change, and on 16 March the power for Local Authorities to make large-scale footpath closures was revoked. This was followed on 22 March by government receiving 'the first formal veterinary risk assessment of the risk that walkers could spread FMD'. There followed a series of initiatives, such as 'Open for Business Campaign', launched on 1 April, and the English Tourism Council's campaign 'England the Great Gateway' launched 6 April.

From that point the government was actively promoting access to the countryside, to encourage visitors. By 22 June it was indicating that, other than in exceptional circumstances, it would expect all Local Authorities to lift all blanket closures except in 3km zones from mid July. Nationally, paths were progressively opened. The relevant figures show 14% by 15 April; 26% by 17 May; 42% by 31 May; 55% by 14 June; 85% by 27 July and 99.5% by 1 March 2002. However, even allowing for this, the effect of the FMD was to substantially reduce access to the countryside for a substantial part of the year.

PUBLIC AND BUSINESS RESPONSE

So far as can be judged, the Government's initial statements and guidance in late February had a profound influence on the general public and on businesses and organisations working in rural areas. Within a matter of days there was a perceptible change in the pattern of public use of the countryside. Many regular visitors paid heed to the Government's urging and, in an effort to minimise risk to farm livestock, simply stayed away.

For rural businesses and organisations too the impact of the initial policy was significant. Farming businesses understandably curtailed their off-farm activities, but more than that many businesses working on the land or located in rural areas introduced precautionary measures to address the perceived risk of spreading FMD. These generally were designed to reduce contacts with the land, to avoid situations that might increase the risk of inadvertent virus spread between people, and to restrict access to land-based facilities, in line with government guidance[79]. Throughout the country - even in areas where there was no FMD - the pattern of response was the same; people were concerned to avoid any possibility that their actions might somehow spread the disease.

We cannot quantify how important were the public and business responses in the early stages after the FMD outbreaks began. However, we think it should be recognised that whilst media images and footpath closures were significant factors affecting visits to the countryside later in the epidemic, in the early stages many people stayed away mainly out of a sense of public responsibility[80].

CLOSURE AND RE-OPENING OF THE COUNTRYSIDE

Effecting Closure

When the new legislation was made on 27 February, the County Council acted quickly to assess the implications for Cumbria. On the 28 February, after receiving veterinary advice from the Animal Health Office, Rosehill and taking soundings with adjacent County Councils, it was concluded that the only way of achieving the rapid large-scale reduction of public access, which was being advocated[81], was a blanket closure. Cumbria has some

7,440km of Public Rights of Way, including 5,450km of footpaths and 1,885km of Bridleways, and a case by case implementation would have been logistically impossible. Thus, a legal declaration was made prohibiting access *'to moorland or public foootpaths or bridleways which adjoin or give access to agricultural land'*[82]. Although, Central Government subsequently revoked the powers for Local Authorities to make large-scale footpath closures, it did not revoke any existing provisions. Thus Cumbria's declaration remained in force, subject to partial revocations made locally, until the final revocation was made on 24 December 2001.

Re-opening

In early March Cumbria County Council officials recognised that procedures to allow the restrictions to be reviewed, and where appropriate lifted, would require close liaison with a range of stakeholders. This led to the formation of a Restrictions Review Team, which met for the first time on 23 March (operating as a sub-committee of the Cumbria FMD Task Force). The Team included representatives from: DEFRA; Local Authorities; Police; United Utilities; NFU; National Trust; tourism; forestry; ramblers; mountaineers; and outdoor activity groups. The group was informal, flexible in membership and directed towards facilitating the re-opening programme. By a process of consensus, over the following months it did hugely important work to that effect.

In the early meetings of the Team, when FMD was still spreading rapidly, it was clear that there was a need for risk assessment before sites could be reopened. However, there was limited scientific advice on how risk assessment should be conducted, and each site location had its own distinctive features. By 30 March the Team had prepared Risk Assessment Guidelines, which were approved by DEFRA, and procedures were developed for the organisations represented to carry out risk assessments in their areas or on their land. By the end of April 120 sites[83] in Cumbria had been opened.

However, it was clear that the site by site risk assessment was proving tortuously slow. To meet the demands of tourism and the amenity needs of the local community, larger areas needed to be opened; the High Fells in particular. Thus, whilst individual risk assessments continued, a strategy was developed for risk assessment of whole Fell areas, and for a system of controlled access at minimum risk. Work on this proceeded through the second half of May with public consultation, preparation of guidance by DEFRA and detailed planning by the County Council. On 9 June five areas of the High Fells were opened giving 65% access to the main summits and utilising 28 access points. Each of the latter was manned by two persons and consisted of a small cabin for shelter and storage plus disinfecting facilities and a map board showing the permitted areas and routes. These access points were maintained until the beginning of August.

Towards the end of June, when the Government announced that all area restrictions should be lifted by 20 July, it was apparent that Cumbria would have to be regarded as an exceptional area, indeed many statements from Government made specific reference to Cumbria being an exception. A large part of the County was still under 3km-zone restrictions and east of the M6 Motorway FMD was still active. Local veterinary advice from DEFRA was that area opening should not be considered in parts of the County where there was a significant density of cattle farms.

This led to a phased programme through which Cumbria was 'reopened' area by area. Each phase involved an extensive postal consultation and an appeal procedure to allow farmers to request path diversions where required. After the first opening, which brought an overwhelming response in public enquiries, a helpline was introduced to deal with each opening phase. In all, 5 phases were undertaken using this approach (Table 8)[84]. The final stages of the opening programme dealt with the North and East of the County and with residual closures that remained in other parts. The blanket ban was lifted on the 24 December although, at that stage, some 833 paths remained subject to individual restrictions.

Table 8. Details of the phased opening of areas in August to November 2001 showing dates, areas, number of consultation letters sent and number of appeals for path diversions.

Phase	Date	Area	Consultation letters	Diversions (Requested: approved)
Phase 1	1 August	Central County	1,342	121: 55
Phase 2 A	8 September	West County	1,143	129: 61
Phase 2 B	13 October	Part of south of County	638	70: 28
Phase 2 C	24 October	Remaining south of County	1,015	49: 20
Phase 3a, 3b, 3c	29 November	Skiddaw range	241	22: 8
Phase 4	4 November	Shap, Pooley Bridge and Kentmere area	469	Not applicable
Remainder	24 December	Remaining areas		

Note: Because of some fresh outbreaks Phase 4 was re-opened before Phase 3.

ACCESS ISSUES

From what we have outlined above it is clear that the crucial decisions and actions, which contributed to the way that the countryside became 'closed', were taken very early in the FMD eradication campaign. It is difficult now to judge the mood of the time but several of those to whom we have spoken have commented that they expected the source of the infection to be rapidly identified and the outbreak to be quickly stamped out. They actively responded to the initial government guidance to stay away from farmland, anticipating that the countryside would be 'closed' briefly whilst FMD was dealt with.

Whether a short-term closure was the underlying intention of the Government's policy or whether the coming national-scale outbreak was anticipated can only be a matter of conjecture. However, the amendments to the Foot and Mouth Disease Order 1983 were apparently part of the Government's overall policy response. We remain unsure about the thinking behind this. The pre-existing version of the Order had a strong provision for either DEFRA or the Local Authorities to close access to Infected Areas. Whether intended or not, the extension of the provision to cover Controlled Areas and the introduction of the 'area closure' provisions sent very strong signals to the Local Authorities urgently to prohibit or severely limit access to the countryside.

We are also are unclear why an assessment of the risk of walkers transmitting FMD was not available or could not have been produced quickly before the change in legislation was made, so that it could be issued to the Local Authorities before they needed to take action. So far as we have been able to ascertain the present DEFRA Veterinary Risk Assessment No 4 '*What is the risk of causing new outbreaks of FMD if footpaths are open to the public?*' was not produced until several weeks into the epidemic[85]. It is a clear and practical 3-page document and serves to underline the limitations of the single sentence included in the Guidance issued to Local Authorities on 6 March.

It is important to say that FMD is not a new disease. A good deal is known about it, although not enough about its routes of transmission. The virus is certainly transmitted via the breath, and this is a major route of transmission in cattle, pigs and sheep. However, the virus can be shed in faeces, urine and contaminated saliva. Accepting this, it is reasonable to conclude that people who have been in close contact with infected animals will pose a much greater risk than those who have not. However, it is equally true that someone who has had contact with infected faeces or urine could inadvertently transmit the virus from one place to another.

The risk from walkers and other members of the public may be small but it is not zero. Thus assertion that *'there is no known incidence of the disease having been spread by members of the public using footpaths or bridleways'*, which we have heard, may be correct but, as is often pointed out, absence of evidence is not evidence of absence. The risk created by walkers and others will depend on the circumstances in specific locations. Virus contamination picked up on boots or clothing and inadvertently deposited on another farm could spread infection; and it is more likely where animals and people can come into close proximity, as is the case in parts of Cumbria.

TOURISM INTERESTS

On numerous of occasions, we were told that tourism businesses felt that they had not been represented in the national political debate over access restrictions and that their interests had not been sufficiently taken into account. 'Tourism had no Ben Gill[86]', was an often-repeated sentiment.

We are unequivocal that there should be full consideration of the wider socio-economic interests in any future decisions on restrictions of access to the countryside, as a result of animal disease outbreaks. However, the view that tourism was not represented in the political decision making seems not to match the facts. We were told in evidence from the English Tourism Council[87] of their close involvement in presenting the industry's interests in various Downing Street meetings. Additionally, the 'chronology of events' presented in the Government's submission to the Anderson Inquiry indicates regular meetings with tourism representatives throughout the FMD epidemic.

We have been left in no doubt that many tourism operators in Cumbria feel strongly that they did not have sufficient influence on the decisions that were made in the 2001 FMD epidemic. However, if their views were not being represented, it was not because the industry lacked political access to the decision making process. Rather, it would seem that the English Tourism Council or the Department of Culture, Media and Sport either failed to consult sufficiently or to register fully the views of the Cumbrian operators and their representative bodies. Whatever the reason, the Cumbrian tourism businesses felt and still feel that they were not being adequately represented at the heart of the decision-making process.

Economic Effects of FMD

CUMBRIA IN OUTLINE

Cumbria is amongst the largest and most sparsely populated Counties of England. It is home to just under half a million people and has an average population density of less than one person per hectare. Approximately 65% of residents live in the larger urban settlements but 35%, the highest figure in England, live in rural or deeply rural locations (Table 9).

Economically Cumbria has a reliance on manufacturing, mainly in the urban areas, and on tourism and agriculture in the rural areas. Employment overall is heavily weighted towards the service sectors, with tourism and public services being major categories. Manufacturing is a substantial employer, particularly in districts such as Barrow and Copeland, but the decline in traditionally key industries, such as shipbuilding and nuclear energy, has resulted in increased unemployment (Table 9)[88]. The proportion of self-employment is on average just below the national average of 12%, but self-employment varies from a little over 6% in Copeland to over 17% in South Lakeland.

Whilst average UK Gross Domestic Product (GDP) per head has grown steadily over the past decade, the GDP of Cumbria has been static or declining. Economic growth in the east of the County has been offset by economic contraction in the west. Over the five years to 2000 Cumbria's GDP reduced from being at the national average to being 9% below. Even in the rural east of the County, where there has been employment growth in tourism and the service industries, many jobs are low paid; earnings in some of these areas are as much as 38% below the national average.

Table 9. Some economic and employment statistics for the County of Cumbria and its Districts. (Figures are rounded.)

	Allerdale	Barrow	Carlisle	Copeland	Eden	South Lakeland	Cumbria
Population & area statistics							
Population (x 000)	96.1	70.4	103	70	50.1	103.2	492.9
Area (hectares x 000)	125	7.8	104	74	215.6	155	682.3
Density(people per hectare)	0.8	9.0	1.0	1.0	0.2	0.7	0.7
Population distribution (%)							
Urban	60	91	73	72	29	56	65
Rural	24	9	14	18	22	24	19
Deeply rural	16	0	13	10	48	20	16
Employment by sector (%)							
Agriculture & related	5	1	2	3	11	4	4
Energy and water	1	1	< 1	1	2	1	1
Manufacturing	22	30	20	38	12	16	23
Construction	6	3	4	7	7	4	4
Distribution, restaurants & hotels	28	21	25	15	28	34	26
Transport & communications	4	5	8	3	9	4	5
Banking, finance & related	12	9	12	10	8	12	11
Public administration & services	19	27	23	21	19	20	22
Other services	5	4	4	3	3	5	4
Employees (x 1000)	28.35	23.61	45.96	24.78	17.28	39.12	179.10
Workforce Statistics (%)							
Unemployed	6.3	7.0	3.8	6.6	1.5	1.7	4.3
Self-employed	10.8	8.5	10.8	6.1	11.2	17.1	11.2

There has also been a substantial fall in agricultural incomes since 1995, and alongside that there has been business diversification, from agriculture into tourism and outdoor leisure, and from both sectors into a variety of value-added enterprises. There are many micro-businesses and a high degree of integration between different sectors of the economy, and between businesses within a sector. Economic disruption in one business could therefore be expected to have consequences in others.

Because of the scale and duration of the FMD epidemic, and the interdependencies between different business sectors (Figure 5), the negative effects of FMD on the economy of Cumbria were substantial and widespread. The direct and indirect effects of the disease on farming and related industries were compounded by the impact of the disease control measures on tourism, and both affected the general economy. Large numbers of businesses suffered a reduction in sales. During the Inquiry we were told how all sectors of business strove to address the fall in income. They cut their input costs and staff costs and deferred or cancelled maintenance work and investment plans. Many were forced to draw heavily on reserves or negotiate bank loans; some temporarily ceased trading.

In line with the importance of agriculture and tourism, FMD reduced the economy of Cumbria by an estimated £266m[89], approximately 4% of the County's GDP. We note that this compares with a corresponding figure of 0.2% for the UK as a whole[90], indicating that in national terms the economic downturn in Cumbria and other FMD affected areas was generally not reflected in the economic activity elsewhere in the country.

AGRICULTURE AND RELATED INDUSTRIES

In a normal year, the gross agricultural output of Cumbria is worth some £480m of which around £315m is livestock and livestock products. In 2001, the estimated direct income loss to agriculture due to FMD culls was about £130m, equivalent to 41% of the total livestock output of the County. Farms, which did not suffer through culls, were faced with adverse trading conditions and additional costs, incurring a further economic penalty estimated to be over £6m. Indirect effects on the wider economy through agriculture were of the order of £30m, with estimated losses of income of £20m in the feed manufacturing and feed supply sectors, over £3m in the agro-chemical sector and over £3m in the engineering sector.

Figure 5. Categories and types of business affect by foot and mouth disease.

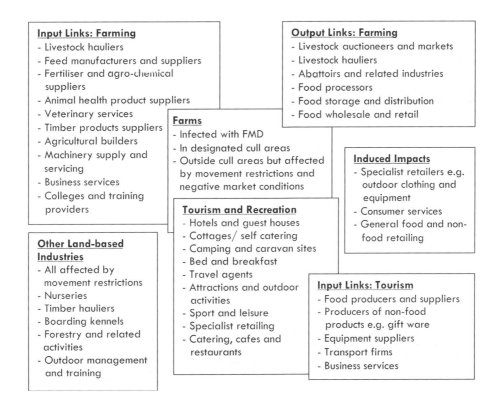

Payments for animals culled under the FMD provisions and the Livestock Welfare Disposal Scheme were estimated to be some £226m and this served to offset the income losses in farming. Taken on balance, the figures indicate there was a positive cash flow into the County's farming of approximately £90m. However, in a survey of 67 farms (53 of which had suffered stock culls) the Centre for Rural Economy (CRE) found 94% of farmers intended to continue in livestock production. Thus the money received in compensation will be mainly re-invested in replacement stock.

The survey also showed that, as compared with the year 2000, farms that had not suffered culls recorded an average loss in gross income of £8.7k, which with the additional costs, gave a net income loss was £14.1k. For farms that had suffered culls the average losses in gross income were £98.2k but consequential adjustments in other areas of income and expenditure, led to net income reductions of £51.5k. However, this figure represents an underestimate of the real effect of FMD since the businesses will take 3-4 years to rebuild their herds and flocks.

The total cost of the farm cleansing and disinfecting in Cumbria was the highest in Britain at approximately £67m. However, this largely reflected the number of outbreaks. Costs per farm in Cumbria were in the mid-range of those recorded elsewhere (Table 10). The Comptroller and Auditor General has estimated that the overall cost of the Watchtree burial site near Great Orton is likely to be £35.1m.

Total payments to disposal contractors throughout Britain were £188.5m. We have not been able to dis-aggregate this total figure, but proportionally it equates to approximately £82m for Cumbria. We note that two contractors, Carrillion and Cumbria Waste received a total of £38.6m for work in Cumbria but other contractors such as Snowie (£38.4m) operated widely both in England and Scotland.

It is difficult to estimate the proportion of these various costs which would have contributed to the general economy of Cumbria. The vast majority of the cleansing and disposal costs represented income to contractors but a proportion of the contractors expenditure would have been in the employment of local labour, displaced from agriculture and tourism.

Table 10. Average costs of cleansing and disinfecting of farms by Disease Control Centre

Disease Control Centre	Average cost per farm (£k)
Worcester	70
Cardiff	44
Dumfries	39
Gloucester	37
Carlisle	34
Newcastle	32
Leeds	31
Exeter	25
Others	26

TOURISM

Tourist spend in Cumbria was £981m in the year 2000; but in 2001 there was a massive reduction in visitor numbers and a consequent effect on revenue. The impact in March was dramatic, with a reported fall in total revenue of 60%. There was a progressive recovery from April to August but even in the later months of the year a 20% reduction was being estimated. Tourism revenue overall was down by an estimated £260m, comprising a direct £200m impact on tourism businesses and a related £60m impact into the wider economy. The reduction in gross income has been estimated to average approximately £50k for each tourism business in the County but that average figure obscures a great deal of variation.

Across the sector, the pattern of impact varied with the type of business and its location. Some town-based visitor attractions remained buoyant. Also the accommodation providers in some locations found there were 'new business' opportunities created by the market demand from disease-control personnel; DEFRA alone spent over £4m on staff accommodation. Surveys in June 2001, when business downturn was still about 25%, showed that the greatest turnover reductions were occurring in bed and breakfast businesses and the smallest in restaurants; by location Copeland was the worst affected District and Carlisle was the least (Table 11).

It would be unwise to over-interpret these figures, but there are several general points that we noted. Firstly, Cumbria's tourism was extremely hard hit by FMD; for many tourism businesses the effects equalled or were greater than those felt within agriculture. Secondly, the impact was experienced well outside the areas of the Cumbria where the epidemic of FMD was concentrated. Finally, and most important, the aggregate economic figures obscure the plight of individual businesses in particular locations. During the Inquiry we heard personal accounts of the microcosm of small businesses caught in the crisis of a market collapse, and of resulting distress and personal hardship. We suspect that economic inter-linkages within an integrated rural economy have not been sufficiently recognised amongst policy makers. If that is so, events in Cumbria are a wake-up call.

Table 11. An overview of the reduction in tourism turnover (%) in Cumbria by business sub-sector and by location (June 2001)[91].

Business Sub-sector or Location	Reduction in Turnover (%)
Sub-sector	
Bed and breakfast	57
Caravan and camping	54
Self-catering	32
Guest house	25
Attraction	24
Hostel	22
Hotel	18
Retail	12
Restaurants	1
Location	
Copeland	66
Lake District National Park	40
Allerdale	40
Eden	35
South Lakeland	26
Barrow	23
Carlisle	13

EMPLOYMENT

Early in the epidemic projections of the potential impacts of FMD suggested that as many as 15,000-20,000 jobs, equivalent to 6-8% of Cumbria's employment could be 'at risk'. However, in practice the increase in numbers of people registering as unemployed was very small, probably less than 700. This difference has been explained by the employment pattern in the types of small business that were affected by the epidemic.

Many of those who work in agriculture and tourism are self-employed or freelance; many are part time workers; and many are casual or seasonal workers whose employment is mobile. Additionally, a high proportion the businesses are 'family concerns' where the tendency would be to reduce hours rather than to lay people off and not to recruit temporary staff for the summer season[92]. Possibly as many as 700 temporary manual jobs were created as a consequence of the disease-control and 'clean-up' procedures, and these would have absorbed some excess labour capacity from agriculture. As a result, it seems that the effect of FMD on jobs was largely absorbed through a reduced recruitment of summer workers and an increased 'under-employment' of workers who were not eligible for unemployment benefit or did not register as unemployed for other reasons.

CENTRAL GOVERNMENT INITIATIVES

In economic terms the Government's policies for dealing with the agricultural aspects of the FMD epidemic involved specific compensation payments to farmers, under statutory or voluntary schemes. Compensation for slaughtered stock and infected materials destroyed because of FMD control programmes was paid under the existing provisions of the Animal Health Act 1981. But, additionally, an Animal Welfare (Disposal) Scheme and a Light Lamb Scheme were introduced as voluntary schemes. These were designed to alleviate animal welfare and market problems arising as a result of the animal movement restrictions and meat export bans.

Early in the epidemic it also became clear that the disease would have impacts outwith agriculture. A Rural Task Force was thus set up to advise the Government on these matters, and during the course of the year a range of measures was introduced to assist the non-farming rural economy. The Rural Task Force comprised representatives from government departments, agencies and stakeholder bodies and was chaired initially by the Environment Minister, Michael Meacher and, after the formation of DEFRA, by the Rural Affairs Minister, Alun Michael. Additionally, from mid-August Lord Haskins was appointed to act as Rural Recovery Co-ordinator and was given a specific remit to consider Cumbria and other areas, which had been particularly hard-hit by FMD.

The Rural Task Force published its final report *'Tackling the Impact of Foot and Mouth Disease on the Rural Economy'*, setting out the impact of FMD and making recommendations for rural economic revival, and Lord Haskins published his report *'Rural Recovery after Foot and Mouth Disease'* on 18 October 2001. These reports have since formed the basis for the national and regional recovery policies that have been put in place[93].

SPECIFIC INITIATIVES[94]

In an effort to ease the financial difficulties of rural businesses and to stimulate business recovery a series of initiatives was taken. As we discuss later, these included the following components.

Deferral of Tax and VAT Payments

From the later part of March the Inland Revenue and the Customs and Excise allowed businesses badly affected by FMD to apply for deferment of any tax, VAT and National Insurance payments they were due to make, with applications being approved on a case by case basis.

Business Rate Relief Deferral and Appeals

Under existing arrangements Local Authorities could provide deferment or relief from rates to businesses suffering hardship and ratepayers had the right of appeal for temporary reduction in rates where the rental value of their property was adversely affected by FMD. Central Government provided additional funding (£20m) to allow the level of relief to be increased from the usual 75% to 95% and in some cases to 98%. And later the rateable value ceiling was increased from £12,000 to £50,000 and the scheme was extended in a number of ways. A 50% mandatory rate relief was introduced for eligible petrol stations and village food shops and for farm properties being used to diversify into non-agricultural activities.

Extension of Small Firm Loan Guarantee Scheme

The Small Firms Loan Guarantee Scheme, which provides guarantees for loans from banks and other financial institutions to businesses whose turnover does not exceed £1.5m (£5m for manufacturing firms), was extended to business sectors not previously included.

Business Recovery Fund

A Business Recovery Fund (£80m) was introduced to provide targeted help for small businesses. The fund was managed through the Regional Development Agencies; in the case of Cumbria through the North West Development Agency (NWDA). The fund was designed to cover measures that would allow viable businesses to improve their prospects after FMD was over, and it specifically excluded payments to assist with cash-flow shortfalls. Grants under the scheme were limited to £15,000 of which up to £7,500 could be used to help meet interest on bank loans. Businesses in the agriculture and transport sectors could not apply to the scheme since it was consider such applications might contravene EU State Aid Rules. There was some flexibility in the way that the scheme could be implemented in different regions. In Cumbria the NWDA provided funding for business marketing and computerisation[95], as well as for bank interest payments.

Charity Match Scheme

Administered through the Countryside Agency the Charity Match Scheme was a means through which Government provided matching funding (£14m) to members of the public, voluntary organisations and charities for relieving hardship during the FMD epidemic. Two organisations in particular established major initiatives under this scheme: the Royal Agricultural Benevolent Institution (RABI) and the Addington Fund. These initiatives were designed primarily to relieve hardships in farming but as the epidemic progressed they began to assist a wider target group.

Tourism Marketing and Publicity.

Additional funding was provided: to the English Tourism Council (£3.8m) for recovery work, including research, information and promotion; and to the British Tourist Authority (£14.2m) for a publicity campaign to attract back overseas visitors.

CUMBRIAN INITIATIVES

Early in the epidemic Cumbria County Council decided that it was imperative to bring together key individuals and organisations to provide a co-ordinated response to the economic and social challenges of FMD and to maximise the County's impact in seeking support and solutions at local, regional and national levels. This led to the formation of the Cumbria FMD Task Force, which held its first meeting on 19 March 2001.

The Task Force, chaired by the Leader of the Cumbria County Council (Cllr Rex Toft and his predecessor Cllr Stuart Young) brought together some 150 people comprising MEPs, MPs, local political figures and senior representatives of regional and local organisations from the public, private and voluntary sectors. At its first meeting the Task Force decided: to communicate its outcomes to the Government and to its Rural Task Force; to seek meetings with the relevant Ministers; and to set up a Task Force Steering Group[96] under the Chairmanship of the County Council's Chief Executive, Louis Victory. At the height of the crisis this group met weekly.

The Task Force established nine specialist teams, reporting to the Steering Group. These were:

- Business Survival Team (Chair by Brian Lightowler, Cumbria Business Link)
- Restrictions Review Team (Chaired by Stephen Greenhalgh, Cumbria County Council)
- Market Expansion (Chaired by Bruce Bennison, Cumbria County Council)
- Tourism Marketing (Chaired by Chris Collier, Cumbria Tourist Board)
- Health and Social Care (Chaired by Peter Tiplady, North Cumbria Health Authority)
- Rural Regeneration Team (Chaired by James Carr, Cumberland Building Society)
- Special Landscapes (Chaired by Paul Tiplady, Lake District National Park)
- Voluntary Funding (Chaired by Kate Braithwaite, Voluntary Action Cumbria)
- Communications Team (Chaired by Brian Hough, Cumbria County Council)

Throughout the FMD epidemic the Task Force, and its Steering Group and Teams, played a key role in assisting and co-ordinating recovery initiatives across the County; it was a crucial element in the early phase recovery activities. It also was active in promoting the cause of Cumbria to Government, in seeking access to Ministers and in making the case for additional resources for Cumbria. Between 19 March and 19 October it met six times to receive reports and review progress. However, it was continuously active through its members and Teams. Amongst other things it:

- issued regular communiqués or correspondence to inform Central Government on the effects of FMD in Cumbria;
- met and made representations to the Prime Minister, Minister of the Environment, Minister for Rural Affairs and Lord Haskins;
- established Cumbria's 'special case' status in the considerations of the Rural Task Force;
- obtained the services of a consultant vet to advise on the protection of heafed flocks;
- worked to ensure that the problems of the agricultural supply sector were recognised and to establish a planning framework encompassing the agriculture and tourism industries;
- pressed for all affected businesses, to receive immediate direct assistance under the Business Recovery Fund, for 100% rate relief and for maximum relaxation of the State Aid Rules;
- made the case for Cumbria's exemption from the lifting of blanket footpath bans and supported risk-assessed opening of access through the Restrictions Review Team;
- pressed for extension of the Match Funding Scheme provided by the Countryside Agency which supported the Cumbria Community Foundation.

However, the greatest single achievement linked with the Task Force came when the proposal for a RAZ programme for Cumbria, developed through the Rural Regeneration Team, was successful in gaining Government approval. The RAZ provides a framework for the long-term development of rural Cumbria, and has planned multi-agency funding support of £274m in the period to 2006. The Minister for Rural Affairs and the Rural Regeneration Co-ordinator, Lord Haskins, have endorsed the plan.

In its format and approach the RAZ is highly innovative, bringing together existing and new resources provided by Central Government to create an integrated programme covering economic, environmental and social targets within a framework of 8 strategic objectives. It will not only break new ground for rural development in Cumbria, it will establish Cumbria as an exemplar for rural development across the EU and internationally. There are many challenges still to be faced in the introduction and implementation of the RAZ programme but during the Inquiry we were impressed by the wholly realistic approach being adopted by those engaged in the programme and by their determination for it to succeed.

Additional to, but not divorced from, the work of the FMD Task Force, many agencies, and organisations in rural Cumbria were hugely engaged during the FMD epidemic in striving to limit the damage to the County's businesses and to plan for economic recovery in the post-FMD period. We were struck by the vigour and speed with which initiatives had been taken and by the practical assistance[97] and moral support that had been given. We noted the strength of engagement of the NWDA from the earliest stages of the epidemic and its overall commitment to rural development[98] in Cumbria. However, we also identified the important roles played by the NFU, Cumbria Tourist Board, National Trust, Forestry Commission, Countryside Agency, Activ8 (Cumbria Business Link), Cumbria Community Foundation, Voluntary Action Cumbria, Council for Agriculture and Rural Life, Cumbria Crisis Alliance, Longtown Action Group, the Churches and others.

BUSINESS PROBLEMS AND SUPPORT

During our gathering of evidence, we received many comments on the problems faced by individual businesses and on whether the business support initiatives taken by Central Government or locally had been of help. Clearly the experiences of each business had been unique to its own circumstances and we would express a caution that our comments are based on our impressions, rather than arising from any objective statistical analysis. In a few instances we received deeply distressing accounts from people who had experienced massive business set backs and who, despite their best and determined personal efforts, had found little useful financial or other assistance in the schemes that were on offer. Their anger and resentment was evident and understandable. We also noted their determination to re-build what had been lost. More generally, the experiences we heard fell into a number of broad categories.

In agriculture, there was evidence of some residual problems in regard to farms that had been culled out under the FMD control measures. These mainly concerned disputes over payments or issues of valuation of livestock or feed (the short period for lodging appeals against valuations had presented difficulties for some families who had been confined to their farms). However, in the majority cases farmers were starting to re-build their businesses. Many seem mainly to be returning to 'what they know', although a proportion are using 'starting from scratch' as an opportunity to make changes in the balance of farm enterprises or otherwise restructure their businesses. There is a widespread appreciation in the industry that farms that did not lose stock through culls were nonetheless badly affected financially by the FMD control measures. There is a feeling that this may have been underestimated. Our own view is that for both culled and non-culled farms the full business impact of the FMD epidemic is unlikely to become clear before 2004 or 2005.

In other sectors, including those related to agriculture, the picture was varied. Businesses providing agricultural supplies and services, including feed and veterinary services and animal health distributors, have been very badly affected and are facing a long period of down-turn until livestock levels in Cumbria are restored. To quote one animal health supplier: 'the animals were my customers and they have gone'. Some of these businesses have substantially re-orientated and restructured as a consequence of FMD. Longer term this may present problems of agricultural-supply capacity in the County, although it would be reasonable to expect that the supply chain will respond to an upturn in market demand.

In tourism and related sectors, significant recovery has occurred but many businesses are still in a re-building phase, and recovery appears be uneven from one location to another. We were made aware of the permanent closure of one significant attraction but in general the tourism 'infrastructure' has been maintained. An exception is that a few on-farm tourist attractions suffered FMD culls, and these will require similar re-establishment times to other types of livestock businesses.

A number of people in non-farming sectors expressed the view that their business should have received Government compensation for losses. In some instances this view reflected a misunderstanding of the nature of compensation paid made to farmers, which is actually a form of compulsory purchase of assets rather than any compensation for consequential loss. We were told that some tourism businesses carried insurance to provide cover for business losses occurring as a result of accidents or outbreaks of human illness unrelated to the business. They found that under the terms of insurance, they were unable to claim for business lost as a result of the FMD.

Concerning the special financial measures introduced by the Government, most of the comments we received were appreciative of the arrangements that had been made in respect of deferments of tax, VAT and National Insurance payments, and also of rate relief. We did not encounter anyone who had made use of the Small Firm Loan Guarantee scheme. The tourism marketing and publicity initiatives undertaken by the English Tourism Council and the British Tourism Authority had been welcomed, but it was felt that they could have been better targeted and that there was a need for more locally focused support[99].

The main complaint, which was repeated, was over the restrictions placed on the Business Recovery Fund. Whilst the funding available was much appreciated several businesses told us that, in the midst of a crisis, marketing and computerisation would not have been their priorities for grant support. Several were also critical of the £15,000 limit on the scheme, of the slowness in funds being paid from NWDA, and on the exclusion of certain types of businesses which had connections with agriculture. These included agricultural transport and tourist accommodation on farms.

Most people also said that they would have preferred financial assistance in 'retaining key skills'. However, this should be interpreted in the light of the employment statistics discussed earlier. The evidence we received from the NWDA was that a grant programme consistent with 'retaining key skills' had initially been proposed but was found to be outside the terms of the Business Recover Fund because of EU State Aid Rules. The latter also accounted for the £15,000 limit in the scheme and for the exclusion of businesses associated with agriculture[100].

Environmental Aspects of FMD

In December 2001, after FMD was eradicated, the Environment Agency published its initial analysis of the impact of FMD on the environment of England and Wales. This indicted that the environmental effects of the disease and the eradication procedures had been quite small and of short duration. Overall there were no significant problems. We were therefore reassured during the Inquiry when the Northern Area of the North West Region of the Agency also told us that 'To date our monitoring of the environment has revealed very few persistent pollution problems have been caused nationally, and none in Cumbria'.

Nonetheless, the control and eradication of FMD did raise a number of environmental issues in Cumbria and took environmental regulation and enforcement into some relatively uncharted areas of operation. We have therefore focussed on how FMD was handled and on the problems that arose. For a technical consideration of the general environmental impact of FMD we recommend the report of the Environment Agency [101].

ENVIRONMENTAL REGULATION AND ENFORCEMENT

The Environment Agency is the main regulator of environmental pollution in England and Wales and is empowered with a wide range of responsibilities under statute. Briefly, it has responsibilities for:

- *water quality, resources and pollution incidents* in respect of rivers, estuarine waters, coastal waters and groundwater;
- *land* in respect of waste management and providing advice to Local Authorities on contaminated land;
- *air* in respect of authorisation of emissions from industrial plants and air quality monitoring programmes.

However, there are several areas of environmental consideration that arise in relation to FMD where the Environment Agency is not the statutory lead body (Table 12).

It should be noted that the Agency has responsibilities for prevention of groundwater contamination from burials of carcasses or ash from pyres. These actions require authorisation under the Groundwater Regulations 1998 and are also subject to the Animal Byproducts Act, which is regulated by DEFRA and controls disposal of animal waste not intended for human consumption[102]. The Environment Agency is also responsible for waste disposal, excepting wastes from agricultural sources, which are exempt from the normal waste management regimes.

Table 12. Areas of environmental considerations that relate to FMD and the lead body responsible.

Area of consideration	Lead body
Government policy and legislation	DEFRA or DoH depending on subject
Environmental health, including air pollution, statutory nuisances e.g. smoke, smell, noise problems	Mainly Local Authority except for major industrial sites where EA regulates emissions to the air
Granting planning permission	Local Planning Authority
Contaminated land	Mainly Local Authority but for some sites EA may take a lead role
Supply of public drinking water	Local Water Company (United Utilities)
Drinking Water Quality	Drinking Water Inspectorate (for public supplies)
Monitoring quality of private drinking water supplies	Local Authority
Sites of Special Scientific Interest and Nature Reserves	English Nature
National Parks	Lake District National Park and Yorkshire Dales National Park Authorities
Access to the countryside	Local Authority
Public health and consumer interests in relation to food	Food Standards Agency

The Agency is not responsible for matters of local air quality control such as those that relate to the burning of carcasses on pyres. This is the responsibility of the Local Authority through

71

its Environmental Health Department. It is regulated under the Clean Air Act 1993 but the Clean Air (Emission of Dark Smoke) Exemption Regulations 1969 allow animal carcasses to be burned if there is no other practical method of disposal. The statutory nuisance provisions of the Environmental Protection Act 1990 also apply, but from the air pollution standpoint there is no statutory requirement for a prior authorisation of a pyre. Finally, we should say that Public Health aspects of environmental pollution fall under the remit of the Public Health Departments of Health Authorities. The Director of Public Health Medicine, of North Cumbria Health Authority, Dr Peter Tiplady presented evidence to us which is relevant here and to which we will also refer later when considering health and community matters.

ORGANISATION AND COMMUNICATION

From the very early stage of the FMD epidemic the Environment Agency's response was guided by its own National Foot and Mouth Task Force Group. This was responsible for co-ordinating functions within the Agency and for formulating the national policies adopted. The Group was represented at the JCC in Page Street, where policy and operational issues were considered with DEFRA, DoH and others. The Agency's incident management procedure involved a direct line of communication from COBR through a National Controller in London, to a Regional Controller for the North West, to an Area Controller in Penrith. Thus, in a way, the Agency's model broadly paralleled that adopted by DEFRA.

When the first FMD case occurred in Cumbria the Agency immediately established a dedicated team of officers to deal with the disease; at the height of the epidemic this team was 70 strong. From the outset the Environment Agency offered its support to DEFRA at Rosehill. However, we were told that communications were 'difficult' until some weeks into to the epidemic when the Disease and Emergency Control Centre was established, which helped 'to establish rapport' and demonstrate how the Agency could add value to managing the crisis.

The Local Authority Environmental Health Departments began to engage with the problems of FMD in early March but found it very difficult to establish communication with the major agencies and to arrange for data sharing. At that time the Chartered Institute of Environmental Health wrote to the Minister of Agriculture expressing concern that Environmental Health Officers were being excluded from exercising their proper role in making risk assessments on matters of environmental health. Later the situation improved and information began to be shared more widely. However, even well into April, collaboration on the monitoring of air quality was not as close as we would have expected.

A somewhat corresponding picture emerged in our evidence from the Director of Public Health Medicine, who had found great difficulty in the early stages of the epidemic in engaging with the statutory authorities. By the later part of March he was so concerned about the lack of public health involvement in carcass disposal problems that he wrote to the Chief Medical Officer seeking urgent advice. However, in early April things improved and the Public Health Department began to become involved and to be consulted regularly about the location of individual pyres.

ENVIRONMENTAL CONCERNS

The main areas of environmental concern which were brought to our attention during the course of investigations related to:

- burial or landfill disposal of carcasses;
- pyres; and
- disposal of farm waste.

The Environment Agency commented that there had been good control over disinfectant disposal, that no long-term impacts had been observed on surface water or groundwater. It also considered that, on balance, the residual adverse effects of FMD on biodiversity were likely to be small.

In contrast, we recorded the concern about biodiversity in the Action Plan *Sustainable Landscapes for Cumbria*[103] submitted in evidence by the Landscape Regeneration Team of the Cumbria FMD Task Force. This document recognised that much of the area of Cumbria had been conditioned by Man's intervention and that recent years had seen a decline in habitat quality and diversity and some damage to and dereliction of the landscape. Moreover, there was a perceived risk that this process might accelerate in areas where the economics of agriculture were poor and FMD had exerted an adverse impact on farm viability[104]. The Landscape Regeneration Team's 'solution' was to seek opportunity in adversity, and to propose a major shift to environmentally supportive land management strategies focused on the distinctive landscape characteristics of different areas of the County. Fundamental to this is the restructuring of support payments to farming and the attraction of additional funding through the RAZ programme. These are discussed in Part 4 of this report.

Carcass Disposal: Overview

Despite the preferred hierarchy of disposal methods, logistical and transport constraints in the early phase of the epidemic resulted in most carcass disposals taking place on farm. Later as landfill capacity was made available it was brought into use alongside the development of the mass burial site at Great Orton. By the later stages of the epidemic, when there was a flare up of FMD in the 'Penrith Spur', the available rendering capacity was greater and most of the animals were disposed of in that way.

On Farm Burial

On farm burial (and also the burial of pyre ash) was subject to a prior risk assessment under the Groundwater Regulations 1998. This took account of:

- groundwater vulnerability e.g. likely presence of clay or other suitable covering material to prevent groundwater pollution;
- proximity to surface water;
- proximity of any known surface or groundwater abstractions in the area;
- proximity to conservation interests and ancient monuments.

Where necessary, English Nature was consulted on nature conservation matters. Information on private and public water supplies was made available by the Local Authorities and included as part of the Environment Agency assessment. The site was investigated by digging trial pits and also was subject to the Good Water Code, which stipulates required minimum distances from streams, springs, boreholes and field drains.

According to the Environment Agency, farm burial was used on 49 farms in Cumbria and following the lifting of FMD access restrictions these sites were visited by Agency and DEFRA to confirm the risk assessment that had been made. Under the terms of the Groundwater Regulations 1998 there is a need for an ongoing monitoring programme, which we were informed could be required for up to 20 years. A specific point of note is that in the early period before SEAC issued its risk advice on BSE, some animals born before 1 August 1996 were buried. We were informed that, where necessary, a further risk assessment is being undertaken to determine if any further action is required.

Landfill

Four landfill sites were used for the disposal of wastes associated with FMD. Hespin Wood landfill accepted carcasses, pyre ash and small quantities of blood from the Carlisle abattoir. Flusco Pike landfill accepted only carcasses and Distington landfill received animal carcasses and leachate[105]. Lillyhall landfill[106] accepted pyre ash and leachate from a mass burial site in South West Scotland and small amounts of contaminated materials such as clothing. The first deposits of carcasses in landfill started at the end of March and pyre ash and leachate deposits are still taking place.

According to the Environment Agency the operational procedures at these sites had ensured that 'no specific pollution' had been caused by the acceptance of FMD material and the risk of FMD spread through leachate has been controlled through alkaline treatment. However, the Agency acknowledged that both the FMD materials themselves and the excavation of the pits caused substantial smell nuisance and there had been around 350 complaints. We also learned from the Environmental Health Department of the problem of smells from the landfills.

Amongst the community we found continued resentment that residents had not been consulted before the landfills had been brought into use and about the degree to which smells from the sites affected their daily lives. There were also concerns over 'health hazards'. It was felt strongly that it had been wrong to bring 'contaminated material' into the area at a time when the farms in the area were free from FMD; and the wisdom of bringing leachate from Scotland to Cumbria was questioned.

Mass Burial

The largest single burial site in the UK is at Watchtree near Great Orton. It was constructed and used at the height of the epidemic as a means of clearing the backlog of carcasses and creating the capacity for the contiguous cull. The site was authorised by the Environment Agency under the Groundwater Regulations 1998 subject to specified conditions. These related to its construction and to the environmental records that must be submitted for environmental monitoring purposes. The facility is designed on a containment principle using the hydrogeology of the site and a system of barriers and drains to safeguard against seepage of effluent.

Watchtree is owned and operated by DEFRA through contractors, but the Environment Agency has had a continuous involvement with the site. It was in attendance during its construction and use in carcass disposal and has a continued monitoring role. The original authorisation was for 500,000 carcasses and when the disposal was brought to a close on 7 May 2001 466,312 carcasses had been received. Of these 96% were sheep, of which two thirds were slaughtered on site. The site also received 12,085 cattle but was prohibited from accepting cattle born before 1 August 1996.

From its inception Watchtree was a highly contentious project. Now the burial pits are capped and landscape restoration work is under way it has the air of a large industrial facility with very little odour. But during its construction and use it brought great disruption and distress to the local communities, including the village of Great Orton. Large numbers of heavy lorries and the pervasive smell from the site were major problems until late 2001. Since the site is government owned it did not require normal local planning approval, and there was little if any pre-consultation. We understand that the facility may be unique in that it will be controlled under the Groundwater Regulations 1998 rather than licensed as a waste disposal facility. There is some concern on the part of the Local Authority Environmental Health Department that this may present longer-term regulatory and enforcement issues.

We learned from the Environment Agency that the leachate from the site was initially tankered to Workington and discharged directly into the Irish Sea through a long outfall. Even accepting the scientific evidence that the procedure had very little environmental impact, we were pleased that it had been discontinued. The material is now processed through waste water treatment plants in Cumbria and elsewhere. According to the Agency there had been 'some minor localised pollution incidents' due to works on the site but these had been rapidly brought under control.

Community reaction to the facility has been almost universally negative. A Community Liaison Committee has been set up as a mechanism to keep those who live nearby informed of developments and to engage them in a long-term plan to restore the site as a nature reserve. However, the measures taken have only been partially successful and there is suspicion about the long-term proposals for the site, and particularly about the prospect of it being re-established for waste or carcass disposal. We were informed that no objection has been raised to DEFRA's retrospective planning 'Notice of Proposed Development under Crown Development Procedures' for the site, which may help to resolve some of the uncertainty about its long term future.

Pyres

During the disease eradication campaign in Cumbria 130 pyres were used in the destruction of animal carcasses. Typically they consisted of the carcasses, plus coal, railway sleepers, wooden pallets, straw bales and diesel oil. The size of the pyres varied with the number of carcasses to be destroyed but a medium size pyre might be approximately 400 tonnes and burn to leave approximately 60 tonnes of ash[107]. Particularly when they burn slowly, pyres give off an acrid smoke containing particulate matter, sulphur dioxide, nitrogen dioxide and possibly other products of combustion such as dioxins, polyaromatic hydrocarbons (PAHs) and polychlorinated biphenyls (PCBs).

As the number of pyres in Cumbria increased smoke became more and more apparent, particularly for communities close to pyre sites. The local Public Health Departments and the Environmental Health Departments sought to obtain information which could guide the siting of pyres and give a better insight into the effects of their emissions on air quality. At that stage no risk guidance was available from the DoH, despite it being requested. A pragmatic approach had to be taken based on the best information available, and it was determined that no pyre would be permitted within 0.5km of a community under any circumstances. Pyres within 1.5km would be accepted provided the weather forecast indicated the plume would be taken away from the community[108]. However, even on that basis, through early April the Public Health Department rejected approximately 50% of the pyre sites proposed.

Matters came to a crisis point when there was a proposal for a mass burn site at Hallburn near Longtown. Public objection to this was very vigorously demonstrated at a public meeting on 12 April and the development of work on the pyre was suspended. Shortly afterwards on 16 April there was a further public protest at a proposed pyre site at Langrigg. At this stage the North Cumbria Health Authority decided it would make a case against pyres on public health grounds.

On 18 April the Health Authority requested MAFF to suspend further burns. With the exception of one pyre near Calbeck that was too far progressed to be stopped, pyres in Cumbria ceased, and the pyre at Langrigg was dismantled. Subsequently, on 24 April, a full risk assessment paper 'Effects on Health of Emissions from Pyres Used for the Disposal of Animals' was published jointly by DoH, DETR, Food Standards Agency, Environment Agency and AEA Technology. However, by then it was too late for Cumbria because the burning had stopped. On the 7 May the Government announced 'no pyres would be lit in England and Wales after this date'.

75

In the period after the epidemic it has been established that the degree of air pollution caused by emissions from pyres caused levels of particulate matter, sulphur dioxide, nitrogen oxides, PAHs, dioxins and PCBs within 2km of pyre sites to be raised above the rural background levels. Nonetheless, they were comparable with the levels typically found in industrial urban conurbations. Inhalation of these levels of substances was therefore considered by the DoH not to present a cause for concern. The Food Standards Agency was also able to confirm that dioxin and PCB levels in foods were, with very few exceptions, within the normal ranges, and that no significant harm was expected from food produced near pyres.

The advice contained in the joint risk assessment published on 24 April broadly supported the pragmatic approach that had been adopted in Cumbria, although there is no doubt that in the early stages of the FMD outbreak some pyres were built closer to communities than would subsequently have been recommended.

Farm Waste

Non-livestock materials on farms where animals had been slaughtered were necessarily disposed of as agricultural waste. This is not 'controlled waste' and therefore falls outwith the regulatory scope of the Environment Agency. We were told by farmers and others of apparent examples of what might be questionable practices in the handling and disposal of materials such as asbestos. We understand that DEFRA has no record of the amounts or locations of waste that was disposed in this way.

Community and Health Impacts of FMD

COMMUNITY

The impact of FMD on the communities of rural Cumbria was enormous, and it affected almost everyone. Family life was disrupted; livelihoods were under threat; social activities were curtailed; and friends became divided by conflicts of view or competing interests. We have heard of the tension in the community, but also of the collaboration, mutual support and community leadership that came to the County's aid when it was most needed.

During our inquiries we received evidence of the many hardships that were faced by individuals and families, and of the distress, frustration and anger (not always in that order) that were experienced. We have been impressed by the commitment and outstanding work of the many groups and organisations that played vital roles in providing practical support and assistance. And we have noted the community appreciation of the many individuals who worked tirelessly to deal with the crisis and fashion recovery and regeneration. The most frequently applied description has been 'it was like a war zone', and few people to whom we have spoken would seem to disagree.

The CRE has undertaken research in the Northern Fells to study how life was affected on farms and amongst those living in rural villages. What emerges from the farm study is the creation of a world of isolation driven by an overwhelming concern to keep the virus at bay; not to leave any opportunity for the organism to be spread by inadvertent contact. Thus families tended to become confined to their farms even before this became enforced by the FMD restrictions. Children were sent to stay away or kept off school. Diversified off farm businesses were closed or kept in operation by the 'away posting' of one member of the family. Visits to family, friends or social venues virtually came to a standstill (Table 13). Concerns and worries induced by the threat of FMD became compounded by worries about the feeding and welfare of livestock. The drop in both farm and off farm income caused financial pressures; and the constraints placed on normal life created family tensions.

In the villages too life was changed. Nearly everyone avoided unnecessary journeys. Businesses, households and community life adjusted to the uncertainties and fears of spread of FMD. Many people could see their livelihood being threatened as businesses struggled with the fall in trade and visitors failed to appear. Village organisations, societies and clubs went into abeyance. Sports and arts events were cancelled. The concerns and uncertainties surrounding how FMD was spread caused almost everyone, not just farm families, to restrict their interaction with others and avoid group activities. In evidence Great Strickland Parish Council wrote: 'Non-farming residents were afraid to travel for fear of spreading infection, leading to wide-scale restrictions on social and business activities. Great Strickland Village Hall, normally at the centre of this thriving community, was not used at all during the outbreak'.

Table 13. Farm household (%) where members were prevented from engaging in their normal activities by FMD restrictions in the Northern Fells[109].

Type of Activity	Farm households (%)
Visiting friends	96
Visiting family	93
Going to the pub	89
Attending shows or fetes	82
Shopping further afield	74
Going to church	72
Shopping locally	64
Attending school	58
Attending special occasions (weddings, christenings etc)	50
Attending off-farm work	46
Receiving health care	9

Communication became very important. Many who had been confined on farms told us that the telephone became a lifeline and Radio Cumbria a valued companion. This was where the voluntary organisations, the churches and other groups played an increasing role creating networks of contacts to provide assistance, responding to peoples' practical needs and in the case of some organisations assisting in getting emergency money to families in need. Many organisations[110] played their part in different ways and at different times during the course and the aftermath of the FMD epidemic. In our view their contribution to the community was immensely important.

A range of charities, organisations and agencies provided funding for community action. These included the Addington Fund; Hadfield Trust; Scott Trust; Council for Agricultural and Rural Life and others. The Cumbria Community Foundation developed and managed the Cumbria Community Recovery Fund[111]. We were informed that the Fund's administration had contact with over 900 families that had experienced significant personal financial hardship, and it had made over 1,100 grants in total. It had also allocated grants to 134 local voluntary and community groups who had experienced a shortfall in funding or a loss of revenue as a result of FMD[112].

 Local Authorities, Health Boards and others also found the FMD control restrictions posed difficulties to the delivery of services. Grass cutting, rubbish collections, pathway maintenance, 'meals on wheels', social services, funeral services and many others raised issues wherever they involved services to farms or access across farmland. In some locations, such as Great Orton, there were even questions about whether the village school should be closed.

The Local Authorities also faced resource challenges. FMD created a range on new demands that needed to be met. For example, Government requested Trading Standards Departments to take on a wholly new area of movement licensing under its animal health responsibilities. Closure and reopening of pathways involved the commitment of a team of staff; Environmental Health Departments and Emergency Services Departments needed to undertake additional work. This necessarily incurred expenditure as well as having lost opportunity costs arising from the deferment of work already planned. We understand that the cost to Cumbria County Council was some £2.1m. We also understand that payment for some work undertaken on behalf of DEFRA may still be outstanding.

HEALTH

Anything that can be said about the effects of FMD on human health must necessarily be qualified by the reservation that the comments are made within the limits of the information available up to the present. In evidence we did not encounter any statistical analysis of health trends that may give an insight into the population effects of FMD. Moreover, at this stage we think it would be difficult to undertake a meaningful trend analysis. More may be revealed in a few years time.

On the basis of the evidence of the Director of Public Health Medicine, there had been no notable increase in enteric disease over the FMD period. However, as indicated by increased subscribing rates for medicines, there had been an increase in respiratory problems, which were assumed to relate to the smoke from the pyres. Generally, however, there does not appear to have been a significant increase in demand on the health services. On the basis of what we learned from the Public Health Departments, Environmental Health Departments or Environment Agency there were also no indications of problems of waterborne infections, although there was clearly concern over the risks that such problems could have arisen.

Our attention was drawn to the specific physical health problems that had been experienced by some individuals. We cannot make any enlightened comment on these cases other than to say that those affected attributed their conditions to their experiences during the FMD outbreak. We also express our best wishes for their early recovery to full health.

We did find evidence of what the Director of Public Health Medicine described as problems of 'emotional, social and mental health'. The situation was well expressed in his comment that some people 'had had too much to bear'. It may not be easy at this stage to quantify this form of health damage, although we suspect that a pattern may eventually emerge in the social health statistics. We can attest from our meetings and discussions that many people had gone through a period of enormous stress created by the circumstances in which they found themselves, and over which they had little control.

Some indication of the scale of this stress was provided in the evidence from Voluntary Action Cumbria, which, during the worse of the crisis, instigated a 24-hour helpline, manned by a team of 8 volunteers to meet the demand for support and assistance. The Citizens Advice Bureau (CAB) was able to provide us with some objective statistical indicators of the problems being experienced within the community. At their office in Wigton the recorded number of enquiries in 2001 was increased by 45% over the previous year. At the office in Eden the corresponding increase was 32% and at Carlisle (which also covers Longtown) it was 30%. These enquiries covered the full range of issues on which CAB provides advice, but we noted that 40% were related to debt, up from about 30% in the previous year.

To gain some further insight into the health problems that may occur the Institute of Health Research at Lancaster University has established a project on the *Health and Social Consequences of the 2001 Foot and Mouth Epidemic in North Cumbria.* Within the study group are included farmers and farm workers, small business operators, 'frontline' workers such as DEFRA staff and disease control personnel, members of the community and health professionals. Results after the first year of this project indicate that FMD has created a significant trauma affecting a range of occupations, and from which recovery in some cases may be problematic.

Although the work is at an early stage, the results obtained so far give cause for concern. In the core study group of 54 people:

- 11.1% have been clinically treated for depression or anxiety;
- 7.4% have a family member who has been treated for depression or anxiety;
- 20.3% are reporting signs of 'post-traumatic experience';
- 44.4% report feelings of anxiety or stress that are not being dealt with;
- 29.6% are reporting on-going health, financial or social problems that they relate directly to the FMD crisis.

We received anecdotal evidence of individual children being emotionally 'withdrawn' during the FMD epidemic but we are not aware of any data that would allow an objective appraisal of any short-term or long-term impact on child health.

Conclusions and Recommendations

Countryside Access

We have heard arguments during the Inquiry that, at the start of the epidemic the Government's position on access to the countryside was over-precautionary. We found it difficult to be certain about the Government's thinking, given the state of knowledge on the location of the FMD virus in the UK at the time. However, there is no question that the risks involved could have been better communicated and should have been supported by an authoritative risk assessment.

We are of the view that the Cumbria County Council was faced with no realistic alternative than to take the action it did in effecting access restrictions and continuing to apply the best advice on veterinary risk assessment as it was received. We were impressed by the work that was undertaken to remove restrictions subsequently, and by the development of risk assessment procedures, including the new mapping technology and consultative approaches used at the various stages of the process. We have concluded that in three main areas there would be benefits from a different approach in the event of any future FMD outbreak.

Firstly, when new powers to reduce access to the countryside were allocated to the Local Authorities they were provided with no meaningful risk assessment guidance from Central Government. Quickly prepared guidance that could have been updated later would have been preferable to no guidance at all. **We recommend that, as a matter of policy, all changes by Government in disease control legislation requiring implementation by Local Authorities should be supported by appropriate risk-assessment guidance.**

Secondly, during the 2001 epidemic there were periods when Central Government was pressing strongly for footpath closures to be removed but in contradiction the advice being given by the DCC in Cumbria was that an accelerated opening of paths would be unwise from a risk management standpoint. **We recommend that there should be closer co-ordination in the veterinary risk advice that is provided nationally by Government and regionally through the SVS Animal Health Offices.**

Thirdly, in any future FMD outbreak, we believe that the Council's action in closing down areas or blocks of pathways should seek to avoid countryside access being prohibited for an extended period, as was the case in the 2001 epidemic. **We recommend that in any future disease outbreak, any general legal declaration covering the closure of footpaths or land by the County Council should be made on a strictly time-limited basis, for example 28 days.**

During our work we have become aware of the legal complexity of matters relating to Rights of Way, Byways, footpaths, cycle tracks and various categories of roads. We have found that there are unresolved legal debates between the Cumbria County Council and DEFRA over the powers to close roads under the Foot and Mouth Disease Order 1983. There are also issues surrounding the most appropriate way to deal with minor roads that are also part of the footpath network.

We cannot suggest how these issues should be resolved legally but we do consider they warrant serious study by government lawyers at national and local levels. We also believe that the present dual arrangements for closures of access routes under the Foot and Mouth Disease Order 1983 should be reconsidered. We are not convinced that DEFRA has the relevant local knowledge to deal with these powers. **We recommend that the appropriate Local Authority (the County Council where that applies) should hold sole responsibility for closures of Rights of Way, or other pathways, under the Foot and Mouth Order 1983, replacing the present arrangements whereby powers are held both by the Local Authority and DEFRA.**

It became apparent during the Inquiry that the value of public access has in general been underestimated both at Local and National Government level. In a County such as Cumbria where the economy is heavily dependent on access we consider there is a need to ensure co-ordination of information, decision-making and planning on access and footpaths between the responsible bodies. This would also serve to ensure efficient use of resources in developing access networks. With this in view, **we recommend that Cumbria County Council build on the work of the Restriction Review Team to establish regular meetings between responsible bodies and key stakeholders to develop methods and policies to protect and enhance countryside access**[113].

Economic Impact of FMD

FMD and related disease control measures had a major impact on the economy of Cumbria originating in the farming and tourism sectors, but quickly permeating into the wider economy. We have been impressed by the speed with which local organisations responded to the developing crisis and set in train systems that would assist a co-ordinated approach. In this the Cumbria FMD Task Force and its related sub-groups played a key role, and many agencies, organisations and individuals made important contributions. Given its effectiveness in achieving common purpose, scaled-down versions of the FMD Task Force would provide a good model to ensure the effective engagement of stakeholders. **We recommend that, where appropriate, Cumbria County Council build on the FMD Task Force model and create similar, but smaller, groups to help take forward initiatives related to the County's post-FMD recovery and regeneration**.

Some tourism businesses carried insurance to provide cover for business losses occurring as a result of accidents or outbreaks of human illness unrelated to the business. However, they found that under the terms of insurance, they were unable to claim for business lost as a result of FMD. **We recommend that tourism organisations advise the industry of the limitations of existing insurance cover and, together with the NWDA, make**

representations to the insurance industry for the development of policies that would provide cover in the circumstances that occurred in Cumbria in 2001.

The effects of the economic downturn on employment patterns in Cumbria were complex. The figures suggest that large numbers of people may have moved into under-employment rather than unemployment. From an economic planning standpoint it is important for the County Council and the NWDA to have a full understanding of the employment drivers so that the links between economic development and jobs can be quantified. **We recommend that there should be a programme of research to provide an improved understanding of the relationship between economic activities and the creation of jobs in the Cumbrian economy.**

The Business Recovery Fund was of limited use because it was restricted in the amount of funding that could be allocated, the types of businesses that were eligible and the purposes for which the funding could be applied. These restrictions all derived from the application of EU State Aid Rules. **We recommend local and central government campaign for greater flexibility in State Aid Rules to allow specific economic emergencies, such as those that occurred in Cumbria in 2001, to be addressed.**

Although businesses are making determined efforts to recover from the effects of FMD, we suspect that many will remain in 'recovery mode' for some time. They will thus have an increased medium-term requirement for support and assistance from the public sector agencies and the Cumbria County Council. This will require detailed and up-to-date information on the changing regional economy, so that initiatives can be carefully targeted to achieve best effect. **We recommend that the NWDA and Cumbria County Council build on existing initiatives to establish an intensive programme of regional economic monitoring that will provide the detailed up-to-date data necessary to allow business support initiatives to be targeted to the needs for economic regeneration.**

Environmental Impact of FMD

The evidence indicates that some of the difficulties encountered during the FMD epidemic related to the fact that the national agencies (DEFRA, Environmental Agency, and DoH) did not 'connect' with the local agencies, such as the local Environmental Health Department and the Public Health Medicine Department. As a result it was several weeks into the FMD crisis before effective working links were established. This is a problem that needs to be addressed, and it is probably best tackled at the local level.

We recommend that Cumbria County Council seek to establish a forum in which the public sector agencies covering environment and health would meet on an annual or more frequent basis. This would be designed to create closer links between the different service providers and to develop an integrated plan for Cumbria covering the areas in which the national and local bodies have responsibilities, including FMD contingency planning.

The way that landfill sites were brought into commission for dealing with carcass material and the Watchtree mass burial site was established, has left a legacy of resentment amongst the nearby local communities. We recognise what was done cannot be undone but we believe that the local residents have a right to expect that their interest should be taken into account. **We recommend that the operators of the Distington landfill and of the Watchtree mass burial site build on existing initiatives to ensure that complaints of smell or other environmental intrusions on the local community are fully addressed.**

Although we were content that the Watchtree is a well designed and well run facility its long-term future gave us significant cause for unease. Many local residents are of the view that the facility has blighted their locality, and they are seeking reassurance over the future plans for the site. Our information from the Environment Agency is that the site will require to be monitored for at least 20 years, so we assume that at the end of the present 5-year management contract some further arrangement will be put in place. We understand that there is a proposal to develop the site as a nature reserve but DEFRA has not been able to confirm to the community that the site will not be brought into use at some stage in the future. In our view the continuing uncertainty over the future of the site is leading to suspicion and distrust, particularly given the circumstances of the site's creation. **We recommend that DEFRA states unequivocally the future plans for the Watchtree site, and particularly whether it is to be permanently closed for disposal of animal carcasses or other waste. Permanent closure would be the plan favoured by the local community and the Inquiry Panel endorses that view.**

We have concerns about the potential for stored up problems associated with some on-farm burials of non-livestock materials during the post-FMD cleansing on farms. **We recommend that the County Council, the Environmental Health Departments, Environment Agency and DEFRA jointly consider what might be done to map where materials are buried and where necessary to address any safety issues that may emerge.**

Community Activities

It is difficult to judge how quickly community activities in Cumbria will fully re-establish. Our impression is that there has been significant recovery but the effects caused by FMD are still being felt. In an area like rural Cumbria community activities make an important contribution to a fully functioning society, and we are strongly of the view that every effort should be made to rebuild or replace what has been lost. We note the strategic plan for the development of community activities under the RAZ programme, and fully endorse the need for dedicated resources to be allocated to this aspect of recovery and regeneration.

Health

There must always be reservations about interpreting the early results of a medium-term research programme, but, with that caveat, the initial results from the University of Lancaster work are disturbing. Moreover, they begin to add some dimensions to the anecdotal information we have received during our public meetings. **We recommend to both researchers and funding bodies that there should be further work into the emotional, social and mental health consequences of FMD in Cumbria, and that the research should be extended to encompass children.** Additionally, we suggest that the health and social welfare departments in the County should closely monitor the results, with a view to introducing effective intervention strategies where appropriate.

PART 4: LOOKING TO THE FUTURE

In this final Part of our report we have looked to the future, focusing our attentions on the development of rural Cumbria, and building on the insights we have gained during the Inquiry. We have not considered the more industrialised areas, such as Barrow and the urban towns of West Cumbria, but some of our observations have general relevance across the County.

Rural Action Zone

One of the positive developments to come out of the FMD crisis was the establishment of the Cumbria FMD Task Force and the Rural Regeneration Team. As a result of the Team's activities a long-term strategy for the recovery and regeneration of rural Cumbria began to emerge at an early stage, and ultimately this was encapsulated in the proposal for the RAZ programme.

The RAZ programme is crucially important to the future of rural Cumbria. It provides a policy and strategy framework not only to repair the damage of the FMD epidemic but also to go further and address the underlying challenges that will face rural Cumbria over the next two decades. The programme clearly needs to be sound in its fundamentals, but it also will require a flexible, innovative and highly effective process of implementation if its objectives are to be realised. We were therefore pleased to hear in evidence that the challenges that lie ahead have been fully recognised and realistically appraised by those closely involved[114].

Based on an analysis of rural Cumbria, the development of the RAZ programme was driven by the challenge of addressing a series of identified overlapping economic, environmental and social needs as shown in Figure 6.

Figure 6. Economic, environmental and social needs identified in the research on which the initial Rural Action Zone proposals were based.

Economic needs
- reducing overall reliance on tourism and agriculture in the rural Cumbrian economy;
- making farming more robustly protected against repeat of FMD or similar;
- spreading the benefits of tourism more widely throughout the County and diversifying its product range, lessening its susceptibility to restricted access;
- increasing the adaptability of the agriculture support and supply industry, retaining more value locally;
- overcoming negative images and rebuilding the reputation of Cumbria as a tourist destination;
- increasing the capacity of local businesses to innovate and benefit from ICT.

Environmental needs
- recognising and building upon the economic and environmental interdependence of agriculture and tourism, particularly in the uplands;
- providing more opportunities for agriculture to become sustainable economically and environmentally;
- increasing the capacity of local businesses to capitalise on the international significance of Cumbria's landscapes.

Social needs
- supporting communities and increase their capacity to benefit from regeneration;
- increasing the skills levels in a diversified rural economy;
- increasing the work-skills and career potential of the Cumbrian workforce;
- addressing the medium and long-term effects of FMD on the health and well-being of the Cumbrian communities.

The initial RAZ proposal was published as a draft strategy *First Steps: A Proposal for a Cumbria Rural Action Zone* in October 2001, only a month after the last FMD case had been reported. Subsequently, the programme was refined and restructured to align its elements with those in the Northwest Regional Recovery Plan *Rural Renaissance*, which was published in April 2002. The second-generation document *Cumbria Rural Action Zone 'Next Steps' Strategy* was completed by the end of May 2002, barely six months after the initial outline proposals had been formulated.

VISION AND OBJECTIVES

The vision of the RAZ is:

To enable the rebuilding and development of a dynamic rural economy for Cumbria, which is financially, socially and environmentally sustainable.

Within the vision, five strategic priorities have been identified. These are:

- developing a diverse, dynamic, competitive rural economy for Cumbria, which is financially, socially and environmentally sustainable;
- improving the environmental quality of land and waters and seeking to ensure that their quality is recognised both nationally and internationally;
- increasing opportunities for all who visit Cumbria to get enjoyment from the countryside, together with its related towns and villages, through improved access and facilities;
- creating integrated, responsive and appropriate services for the communities of rural Cumbria through working together; and
- sustaining the cultural landscapes of Cumbria which are already recognised both nationally and internationally for their visual and spiritual qualities.

These priorities have then been captured in 8 targeted strategic objectives (SO), which provide the programme's framework for action. The objectives and their rationales are as follows.

- *SO1: Broadening the Economic Base of Rural Areas.* While agriculture and the primary industries provide an important backbone of the rural economy, significantly greater added value and wealth is created by other sectors. Rural areas remain less diversified than their urban counterparts. To broaden the economic base of the rural economy, this SO seeks to enhance inherent wealth generating capacity and employment opportunity, appropriate in scale and nature to local circumstances.

- *SO2: Renew & Strengthen Sustainable Recreation and Tourism.* It is imperative that the competitive position of the regional tourism product be improved, enhanced and broadened to attract an increasing share of this growing market. This SO is designed to provide a generic framework within which partners can seek to achieve these ambitions while recognising the interdependence between tourism and landscape, and ensuring adherence to sustainability principles.

- *SO3: Assisting the Restructuring of Agriculture.* With reducing income from traditional farming, many of those wishing to retain involvement in agriculture will find it necessary to generate income from a broader range of activities. This SO is designed to assist an efficient and effective transition within agriculture, building upon existing structures. This will enable improved efficiency, environmentally friendly diversification appropriate to local circumstances, and multi-functionality through agricultural business reviews, planning, diversification and training.

- *SO4: Enhancing the Competitiveness of Primary Agriculture.* Despite the commercial pressures expected to bear on the agricultural sector over the next decade, large numbers of existing producers are likely to seek continued involvement in primary agriculture. Long-term survival will require a process of continuous efficiency improvement and enhanced competitiveness. This SO is intended to assist primary producers within the region to adapt to changing circumstances and enhance their capability to compete.

- *SO5: Rural Skills Development.* Workforce skills are vital to the competitiveness of all businesses. This SO is designed to ensure that the process of strengthening the primary agriculture base, restructuring and diversifying the rural economy, and broadening the economic base, is supported by commensurate development of human capital.

- *SO6: Development and Promotion of Countryside Products.* The development and promotion of local countryside products offers significant potential for producers to establish differentiated brands, develop new and alternative markets and generally add and retain value locally. To renew and accelerate the potential benefits from such activities this SO is directed towards assisting marketing and consumption of local products that sustain the environmental and cultural heritage of the region.

- *SO7: Sustaining the Rural Environment.* Rural communities are custodians of an environmental inheritance. Such has become the economic value of that inheritance that it is in the long-term interests of those communities to ensure environmental sustainability. This SO seeks to promote a range of actions designed to ensure environmental sustainability remains a key feature of all forms of structural change and transition in rural economies.

- *SO8: Delivering Social and Community Regeneration.* A growing volume of development research and practice emphasises the role of social capital, community relations and very local organisations, such as voluntary sector organisations, churches and congregations, in sustaining rural regeneration policies and programmes. This SO seeks to support the social infrastructure of rural areas through maintenance of service infrastructure, addressing particular forms of exclusion and invigorating support networks.

The proposed intervention activities that are planned under these strategic objectives are wide and varied and cover very many aspects of rural development for agriculture, tourism and the broader small business sector (Table 11). The interventions also reflect different types of support and assistance from infrastructure and equipment procurement to business advice and training. The proposals are in close harmony with a range of the relevant rural policies including the Rural White Paper, the England Rural Development Plan, the proposals of the Policy Commission for Food and Farming, and emerging approaches to Area Based Initiatives and Local Strategic Partnerships[115].

FUNDING, COSTS AND IMPACTS

Part of the uniqueness of the RAZ programme is that it provides flexibility to create multi-agency funding alliances to support projects. This offers the prospect of reducing or removing organisational barriers so that the full power of the resources that are available can be directed at achieving the programme objectives. The proposed funding for the programme thus brings together a range of existing funding resources, which will be supplied through the agency budgets, and a projected acquisition of new resources to fill the gaps in some areas of the programme. The current funding projections for the initial 5-year period are as shown in Table 12.

Table 11. An outline of the intervention strategies that are proposed under the eight Strategic Objectives of the Rural action Zone Programme.

Strategic Objective	Proposed Areas of Intervention
SO1: Broaden the Economic Base of Rural Areas	- Small business advice and development services - Small business funding - Quality assurance - Infrastructure – land and buildings - Information and computer technology
SO2: Renew and Strengthen Sustainable Recreation and Tourism	- Visitor facilities - Visitor transport - Marketing and promotion - Information and computer technology
SO3: Assist the Restructuring of Agriculture	- Farm business advice and development services - Woodland diversification - Agricultural support industry regeneration - Upland farming support programme - Lowland farming support (linked with SO7)
SO4: Enhance the Competitiveness of Primary Agriculture	- Demonstration farms and promotion of best practice - Farm collaboration and marketing groups - Organic farming network - Farm information and computer technology
SO5: Rural Skills Development	Skills development within - rural businesses - tourism - farming - environment and land management - rural communities
SO6: Development and promotion of countryside products	- Development of Cumbrian products - Promotion, marketing and sales of Cumbrian products - Community product support programme - Collaborative marketing
SO7: Sustain the Rural Environment	- Access enhancement - Integrated land management - Water, river and lakes quality - Environment and conservation programme - Development of Cumbrian uplands
SO8: Deliver Social and Community Regeneration.	- Social and community infrastructure - Empowering Cumbrian communities - Community financial support - Retention of rural services - Community information and communication technology

At this stage, the funding requirements for most of the strategic objectives appear to be largely met from the resources projected to be available. The main exceptions are those concerned with developments in sustainable recreation and tourism, under SO2, and social and community regeneration, under SO8. In both these areas significant funding is still to be acquired.

On the basis of present projections, the RAZ programme has been estimated to increase the Gross Value Added into rural Cumbria by £151m per annum and to safeguard a further £180m per annum. It has been projected that it will create 5,180 new jobs, as well as safeguarding a further 6,270 jobs in rural Cumbria over the 5-year period 2002-2007.

Table 12. Indicative funding (£m) for the Rural Action Zone strategic objectives, total resources available, estimated costs and funding to be acquired. (Figures are rounded to the nearest £ 0.1m.)

Partners or funding sources	SO1	SO2	SO3	SO4	SO5	SO6	SO7	SO8	Total
ERDP/DEFRA	3.3	2.8	4.6	1.6	0.7	3.4	62.4	1.0	79.6
Countryside Agency	2.8	4.0	0	0.1	0	0.1	1.4	2.5	10.8
Forestry Commission	3.9	0	2.0	0.7	0	0	2.0	0	8.5
LSCs	1.2	1.8	7.3	1.8	4.2	2.4	0	0	18.8
NWDA	24.8	7.5	13.2	2.1	1.6	11.0	6.3	0.6	67.0
English Nature	0	0	4.5	1.3	0	0	0.2	0	6.0
EU Objective 2	1.0	4.4	0	3.3	0	2.6	0	0.7	11.9
EU Objective 3	0	1.5	0	0.7	1.5	0	0	0.1	3.8
Leader+	0.3	0.3	0	0	0.1	1.3	0	0	2.0
Private sector	2.1	6.4	19.8	0.1	0.8	1.2	0	0	30.3
SBS	1.5	0	0	1.0	0	0	0	0	2.5
Other	0.1	2.7	0.4	0.2	0.2	0.3	0.1	0.1	4.0
Total	**40.9**	**31.3**	**51.7**	**12.8**	**9.0**	**22.3**	**72.4**	**5.0**	**245.3**
Projected programme cost	**38.5**	**56.0**	**50.9**	**13.6**	**10.3**	**22.1**	**71.8**	**11.0**	**274.2**
Funding to be acquired	(2.4)	24.7	(0.8)	0.8	1.3	(0.2)	(0.6)	6.0	28.9

IMPLEMENTATION AND DELIVERY

The partner organisations in Cumbria have concluded that implementation of the integrated ideas underlying the RAZ is beyond the capacity of the present delivery infrastructure. A Cumbria Rural Regeneration Company is therefore being established to oversee the programme. This will be a small independent not-for-profit company, limited by guarantee and with a Chairman from the private sector. It will not generally be involved in the delivery of projects but it will have the main responsibility for project development and implementation and to act as a 'one stop shop' for project delivery organisations.

It is planned that the company will become operational by 1 October 2002, initially for a five-year period but probably extended to ten years. It will be staffed by a combination of new appointments and staff on secondment from partner organisations. Support in project appraisal, grant administration and monitoring will be given by a 'Regeneration Support Team' provided by Cumbria County Council, which has also agreed to act as the Accountable Body for the financial delivery of the programme. Stakeholder input to the company will be provided by the Rural Strategy Sub-group of the Cumbria Strategic Partnership, which provides an overarching framework for economic regeneration across the rural and urban areas of the County. The Partnership has an important role in the scrutiny of programme delivery and in co-ordination between agencies within and outwith the County.

Considerations of the Inquiry

RAZ OVERVIEW

The RAZ is highly innovative, and it is a credit to all those involved that the proposals emerged and were progressed so quickly even when Cumbria was still struggling to rid itself of the last of FMD. Although firmly based on the familiar principles of economic, environmental and social sustainability, the proposals are refreshingly free from intellectualised sustainability theory. Rather they represent a practical and well-focused strategy to address the needs of rural Cumbria. They have a strong emphasis on local targeting, local partnerships and community involvement, all of which seem correctly to build on the community strengths of Cumbria. We have considered specific aspects of the proposals in later sections but we should first make three overarching observations.

Firstly, in our discussions with various stakeholder groups we have noted the sense of common purpose that has developed during the 'fight against FMD'. We think this is a valuable asset and provides a basis from which to build their involvement in the RAZ programme.

Secondly, we have registered that there are some 45 organisations operating in Cumbria mainly in economic, social, environmental and community fields; in evidence we have been told there are 176[116] different partnerships and some 77[117] different funding streams. We acknowledge there may be the benefits from the innovation resulting from a rich pattern of organisational and partnership diversity, but we suspect that the degree of diversity in Cumbria could be confusing to client groups and possibly inefficient in use of resources. This is a matter that we believe it will be important for the RAZ to address.

Finally, we have heard a good deal of praise and support for the RAZ initiative amongst the stakeholders groups but we have also been made aware of a concern (we think reasonable concern) that the programme runs a risk of becoming bogged down in 'organisational bureaucracy'. We can only express the very clear opinion that we believe the programme is too important to the future of rural Cumbria for any bureaucratic impediments to be allowed to create barriers to rapid progress.

AGRICULTURE

We have considered the future in terms of the risk of FMD earlier in Part 2 of this report. Here we have focused on the matters that relate to the more general aspects of the future of agriculture and to the RAZ programme in particular.

Since the publication of *Cumbria Rural Action Zone 'Next Steps' Strategy,* the Curry Report proposals have been broadly accepted by Government and the Treasury has agreed the funding necessary for their implementation. Sir Don Curry has been appointed to head a new body that will oversee the changes proposed under the new agricultural strategy. However, the details of the strategy itself will not become precisely clear until the Government publishes its *Sustainable Food and Farming Strategy,* later in 2002.

Quite separately, the European Commission (EC) announced in July its proposals for the EU mid-term review of agriculture. These will not become firm proposals until autumn 2002 and will not come into force until 2004. Moreover there is every prospect that the initial proposals could alter in detail in response to the reaction they provoke from EU Member States.

Thus both the 'Curry proposals' and the EC proposals are likely to be modified as they are brought forward for implementation, and in agricultural policy the devil is often in the detail. However, both sets of proposals have some similar underlying themes, and overall the policy framework for England that will emerge seems likely to place emphasis on:

- reform of the Common Agricultural Policy (CAP), with an increase de-coupling of aid payments from farm production support;
- some shift in the funding from agricultural support to rural development support;
- more emphasis on farm aid payments supporting objectives of 'public good', such as environmental management, animal welfare, and food quality programmes;
- encouragement for agricultural production to be more market-led and responsive to the consumers;

- encouragement to increase the market value of farm outputs by capturing specific markets, providing quality assurance, creating brand identities and adding value through processing.

Against this type of policy framework the RAZ proposals concerning agriculture are relevant and well targeted, and the major question is whether the programme can deliver an agricultural industry in Cumbria that is sustainable and competitive under the emerging policy frameworks. This objective will depend on the selection of the most relevant projects under the RAZ programme, on farmers' resourcefulness and willingness to change, and on the constraints imposed by land type and climate.

Farms in the most productive lowland areas of Cumbria have the potential to compete globally, but farms in the marginal upland areas are facing a difficult struggle and are unlikely to be competitive in commodity markets. Thus, whilst many lowland farms may have choices as to whether they decide to become low-cost commodity producers or specialised producers for higher priced markets, farms in the marginal areas have limited options.

Within its programme structure for agriculture the RAZ adopts a conventional UK approach in addressing the need for change. Thus the main thrust of the programme is based on improved training, demonstration projects, better business advice and grant-funded assistance with specific business initiatives meeting the criteria of the scheme. Whilst this reflects proven 'dissemination and diffusion methodology', widely used in agricultural extension work, the approach may not be sufficient to achieve the change required over the short time scale envisaged. Alternative approaches, such as the 'participative research' programmes[118] employed in some of the Commonwealth countries, would provide a more radical intervention regime and in our view should be considered at the project level.

In either case there is a fundamental need for RAZ projects to be based on a detailed quantitative understanding both of agricultural production in Cumbria and of the markets for its products. Facilitating 'producer clusters' and farmer co-operation is a key task. Only by that means will it be possible systematically to address the challenges of developing new markets, product branding, and adding value by product differentiation or processing. In national or international terms the scale of agricultural production in Cumbria is very modest, and in most sectors the best opportunities for Cumbrian products will come through targeting specific markets of intermediate size. A plus factor is that there are strong regional markets in the UK, which have yet to be addressed.

Cumbrian agriculture already has a significant degree of success in maintaining biodiversity and managing the environment although there can be little feeling of complacency. Some evidence to the Inquiry expressed the view that the rate of environmental gain from the Environmentally Sensitive Area (ESA) schemes had been disappointing. Also there is scope for further development[119], including on some of the more intensive lowland ground[120]. We noted the well-developed proposals for forestry and woodlands contained in the submissions by the Forestry Commission[121] and the landscape and biodiversity emphasis in the submissions of the National Trust and English Nature.

We regarded the environmental, biodiversity and landscape aspects of the *First Steps* RAZ programme to be well articulated and it seemed that they would be well promoted by the relevant agencies. However, these subjects have assumed a lower focus in the *Next Steps* RAZ proposals, although they are an inherent component of the sustainability theme that underpins the whole programme and have specific coverage in SO7. From our perception it will be important that the RAZ does not lose sight of the triumvirate of economic, environmental and social objectives on which it is based.

Our main uncertainties and concerns relate to two specific matters. The first is the economic vulnerability of the cultural land heritage of upland Cumbria, which has a specific dependence on hill sheep and cattle. The second is the way that the Curry Report's proposals and the potential changes in CAP may affect that vulnerable sheep and cattle sector. Until the final details of these two sets of proposals are known it is difficult to make precise judgements about their likely impact. However, the Curry report proposed rates of modulation on agricultural aid should be increased towards a maximum figure of 20% by 2006-2007. At the same time it was suggested that the present range of environmental schemes should be replaced by a single scheme with an entry level providing for a 'broad and shallow' environmental management scheme which would be available to most farmers.

Our present assessment of these proposals is that the modulation changes will benefit a small proportion of farmers but will represent a loss of grant funding for the majority. Further, the redistribution of funding needed to introduce a 'broad and shallow' environmental scheme may benefit many lowland farmers but may disadvantage those in the uplands, many of whom are already engaged in one of the higher level environmental management schemes. Thus, for the most vulnerable sectors of Cumbria's agriculture, the period of transition to a new agricultural policy framework could exacerbate economic pressures that are already very evident.

Cumbria has a unique importance in Britain's land heritage, because of its open Common Lands and the related use of heafed flocks in the land management system. After FMD there is a need for regeneration of heafed flocks. This will take several years and is likely to raise a range of new, and in some cases unexpected, problems. Early indications are that tick borne diseases may be problematic in animals not acclimatised to the Fells.

In an era when shepherds are few in number, some strategic fencing may be needed to facilitate re-heafing. This is likely to be highly contentious particularly in areas that are regarded by many as the last 'wilderness' parts of England. However, some transitional human intervention in the traditional land management system will be essential for the unique land heritage of Cumbria to be maintained. Much of this effort will be commercially uneconomic and will require public funding in support of land heritage, landscape and environmental management objectives. It will also need effective public communication, and possibly temporary legislative derogation, since in the short term fencing may restrict access.

TOURISM

Cumbria has a strong tourism sector based principally on its scenic beauty, environmental quality and ability to provide outstanding opportunities for relaxing in the outdoors. It has been a well-established tourism destination for centuries, and some of its sub-brands, such as 'the Lake District' are internationally renowned. Cumbria as a whole has been recognised as the world's first Green Globe tourism destination.

The RAZ programme identifies the need for Cumbria's tourism to be sustained and developed through investment and through broadening the range and increasing the quality of the facilities and resources available. However, below those headline-objectives there are some challenging issues related to the visitor numbers and tourism-value relationships and the need to protect the environmental resources of the County. Within the area of the National Parks potential increases in tourism value must be seen in the context of restrained increases in visitor numbers. In other areas of the County visitor numbers and tourism-value can be increased hand in hand, taking account of the need to avoid over exploitation and to protect Areas of Outstanding Natural Beauty (AONB)[122] outside the Parks.

Overall, the proposals for tourism development set out in the RAZ programme are sound and well targeted. However, arising from what we have learned during the Inquiry, we would emphasise the need to broaden the range of tourism and visitor facilities and to increase cultural and other events. The objective should be to provide the County with a more varied tourist appeal, whilst maintaining the quality of the natural and cultural heritage. The relatively narrow base of the existing tourism industry was dramatically highlighted by the FMD crisis, but it could also be regarded as an underlying weakness in the County's competitive position relative to other tourism destinations.

During the Inquiry we have noted the diverse nature of the tourism industry, its many small businesses and the complexities deriving from the structures and remits of the different national and local tourism bodies. At national level the British Tourist Authority is responsible for overseas marketing, whilst the English Tourism Council acts as the lead body for the Regional Tourist Boards, as well as undertaking centralised marketing initiatives, work on industry standards, collection of statistics and research. At the next level the Regional Tourist Boards have responsibility for specific geographic regions, providing various guides, advertising and support services, but there are also sub-regional 'brands', which understandably wish to promote their own location.

In Cumbria, the Cumbria Tourist Board (CTB) is the regional body but there are sub-brands representing Keswick, Carlisle, Eden, West Coast and Furness, and there is stakeholder interest in CTB arising from its funding bodies (National, Regional, County and District levels) and from its elected commercial membership. From our perception this results in a difficult balancing of interests. Brand promotion tends to be based on areas rather than products and the agenda for promotion is inevitably mainly influenced by the accommodation sector because of its membership strength.

To consider whether it would be better for the tourism bodies to be structured in a different way is beyond our remit. However, given the structures that exist we have concern over the funding gap that is presently identified in the RAZ SO2. Although the CTB does a first rate job of promoting regional tourism, we have reservations about the industry's capacity to articulate shared goals and work in concert to achieve them. We therefore suspect the industry will face significant challenges in focusing its efforts to secure the development funding it requires.

OTHER BUSINESS SECTORS

There has been long-term recognition of the need to broaden and strengthen the economic base of rural Cumbria, to raise skills levels, and to seek to attract a greater proportion of high-wage jobs. These objectives are reflected in SO1 and SO5 of the RAZ programme. They are mainly targeted at the small business sector and build incrementally on the economic base that exists at present. There are specific provisions for new business starts and for business expansion schemes, but there appears to be an underlying assumption that business development will take place mainly in rural-related, tourism, craft or culturally creative industries.

We were interested in the basis of this assumption, given the recognised attraction for technology and knowledge-based businesses to locate to areas of high environmental and life-style quality. Such companies also seek the infrastructure and supply of skilled personnel and knowledge services (mainly research and consultancy support) to meet their needs. However, the infrastructure issues do not vary greatly with the type of business, and they have largely been addressed either in the Economic Strategy for Cumbria or in the RAZ programme (particularly for ICT). We have therefore directed our attention to the issues of skilled labour supply and provision of knowledge services.

From the evidence we have received, Cumbria has a strong primary and secondary education performance with attainments at GCSE levels in English, Maths and Science that are well above the average. However, post-sixteen education rates are not particularly good and entry rates into Higher Education (HE) are 16% below the average for England, low even for a rural county. Cumbria lacks a comprehensive HE provision, although courses are offered through a range of regional HE institutions within and outwith the County, and also through the Further Education (FE) sector (Table 13). The HE institutions would also normally be the major suppliers of research and consultancy services to business, but the evidence indicates that there are few Cumbria based research and consultancy groups.

This leads us to the conclusion that the limits of provision of HE and associated services in the County are significant constraints on economic development. We have become aware during the Inquiry of the efforts to attract knowledge-based companies and advanced-technology manufacturing to the rural East of the County, and to revitalise manufacturing in the urban West. From our perspective there is a critical need to recognise the close inter-dependence of these initiatives and the further development in the County's framework for HE.

Table 13. Centres for the provision of Higher Education services to Cumbria.

Higher Education Institutions		Further Education Institutions	
St Martins College	Lancaster	Carlisle College	Carlisle
	Ambleside	Lakes College	Workington
	Carlisle	Kendal College	Kendal
	Barrow	Furness College	Barrow
	Whitehaven		
	Kendal		
University of Northumbria	Carlisle		
Cumbria Institute of Fine Art	Carlisle		
University of Central Lancashire	Penrith		
Lancaster University	Lancaster		
Westlakes Research Institute	Whitehaven		
Open University Study Centre	Penrith		

SOCIAL AND COMMUNITY REGENERATION

We welcome the emphasis on social and community regeneration in RAZ SO8, since we have formed the view that continued efforts will be needed to restore the community functions in the wake of the FMD. Several of the approaches outlined in the programme are innovative and will provide new community opportunities.

There is a significant degree of expectation of the benefits of the RAZ amongst the community groups, and efforts should be made to capture the present enthusiasm and drive for re-establishing community activities. We have noted the projected shortfall of funding in the programme on Social and Community Regeneration and suggest that plans for addressing this should be put in place at the earliest stage of RAZ implementation.

Conclusions and Recommendations

RAZ in General

The development of the RAZ programme in the aftermath of the FMD crisis has been a remarkable achievement for Cumbria. Although it has lost a little of its urgency of focus as it has developed to the *Next Steps* stage, we have sensed during the Inquiry that the initiative has captured a huge amount of commitment and energy in the community. We believe that this is something that should be built on and **we recommend that the RAZ should be promoted internationally as an exemplar of good practice in rural development.** This approach would serve not only to maintain the profile of the programme and the commitment of those involved but it would create international interest in Cumbria with benefits to the marketing of the County's goods and tourism.

We believe that the already diverse range of partnerships and projects will increase under the RAZ programme and that there is a risk of confusion amongst the client groups involved in the programme. **We recommend that at the earliest possible stage the Rural Regeneration Company establishes a publicly accessible database of all the projects and partnerships operating in Cumbria, with outline details of the work being undertaken.**

Agriculture

Agriculture in Cumbria is facing a period of very considerable challenge, which is reflected in the provisions in the RAZ programme. There will be a need to create industry clusters and to foster co-operative ventures to address many of the challenges of capturing specific markets, providing quality assurance, creating brand identities and establishing value-added processing. The emerging agricultural policy emphasis on de-coupling of aid payments from farm production, the modulation from agricultural support to rural development and the restructuring of the present grant schemes for environmental management may result in less favourable economic conditions for many of Cumbria's most vulnerable farming businesses.

Policy and market changes are inevitable but the RAZ programme should facilitate the change process and allow a strengthened agricultural sector to emerge. We consider there is a crucial need for robust research on the production capabilities and market opportunities for Cumbria's agriculture so that the RAZ projects can be well targeted to achieve success. **We recommend that 'participative research' techniques be evaluated as a means of project implementation and that an 'Agricultural Strategy Committee' is established as an interface between the RAZ organisation and the farming industry.**

Tourism

We believe that the overall proposals contained in the RAZ programme for the development of the tourism sector are sound. In particular, we agree that there is an important need to broaden the range and increase the quality of the tourist attractions and visitor facilities available. However, we are concerned about the industry's capacity to focus its efforts to secure the development funding it requires. With this objective in view we believe that there is need for a body, reflecting all aspects of tourism, with an independent Chair from the private sector, to create a framework within which the industry can define its priorities and seek consensus. **We recommend the formation of a Cumbria Tourism Forum, with an independent Chair from the private sector, to facilitate the different sectors of the industry in co-ordinating funding bids related to the RAZ programme.**

Other Business Sectors

In our view the absence of a coherent provision of higher education in the County places Cumbria at a substantial development disadvantage, since it leads to a relatively low-skill economy with constraints on growth in new sectors. It almost certainly contributes to the low business start up rate in the County, impairs the ability of indigenous companies to develop and acts as a disincentive to higher-value inward investments.

We believe that the creation of a new HE institution in Cumbria at the present time would be an unrealistic objective. Moreover, we are aware that under auspices of the Advisory Group for Higher Education in Cumbria there have been discussions about closer co-operation between the present HE providers. In our view it will be difficult for the institutions themselves to provide the focus and drive needed to address the problems that Cumbria faces. The County of Cumbria is only a part of their wider market. Rather we believe that the County Council and NWDA should take a lead in establishing a framework organisation, which would act as a focus for HE activities in Cumbria and through which affiliated HE institutions could seek a greater co-ordination of their activities.

The detail of this would need to be explored with the HE partners. However, we have in mind a small not-for-profit company established as a 'Cumbria Institute', which could provide a point of focus for HE provision, including distance learning, and could develop funding for Cumbria-based research and consultancy in support of industrial development. Such an arrangement would bring considerable benefit to Cumbria but it would also add value and create new opportunities for the HE institutions with a presence in the County. Thus, **we recommend that the concept of a 'Cumbria Institute' be explored with a view to advancing the development of higher education, research and consultancy in Cumbria.**

Social and Community Regeneration

Our general view is that the Social and Community Regeneration programme will go a considerable way to re-establishing the community frameworks and networks that have been damaged or lost during the FMD epidemic. However, we have genuine concerns that there are deeper societal effects that may be difficult to address.

During our collection of evidence about the crisis we became conscious of repeated underlying themes, which we can best summarise as follows. - The remoteness of central government from farming practice caused great problems. The administration appeared out of touch with the realities of farming and rural life, and sometimes expressed surprise at traditional practices. The effectiveness of politicians in practical everyday business management was called into question. Decision-making was centralised when it would have been better devolved within an overall plan. All sectors of the community felt distaste for the political point scoring that had emerged during the crisis, and they were angry that the legitimate protests from Cumbria over the disease control problems had taken so long to be heard.

These points did not appear to be made from any party political standpoint. Rather the feeling was that successive administrations had failed to address the problems of farming and the rural areas. Thus, rather than being the sole stimulus for the views expressed, the FMD crisis had served as a point of focus for much that had gone before. We recognise what we witnessed will have a resonance in rural communities in other parts of Britain, but Cumbria has a degree of remoteness that serves sharply to accentuate the issues.

The challenges facing agriculture and the rural areas of Britain are difficult to overestimate, and there are pressing needs for government policies to be formulated from a practical understanding of the problems. However, reflecting Britain's population distribution, urban issues often dominate political priorities, and there is a need to find ways of raising awareness and understanding of rural agendas. The community networking established under the RAZ could have an important role in allowing rural communities in Cumbria to formulate and articulate their views. Therefore **we recommend that within the RAZ programme there should be a Rural Agendas project designed to facilitate community action and leadership on rural issues.**

Appendix 1. Some indicators of the land characteristics of the County of Cumbria[1].

Characteristic	Indicator
Land and Agricultural Holdings	
Total agricultural land area (ha)	577,093
Area in land holdings (ha)	459,093
Common Land (ha)	118,000
Grassland (% total agricultural area)	71
Land in crops (% total agricultural area)	4.8
Number of agricultural holdings	6,220
Farm Types (% holdings)	
Cattle and sheep (lowland)	27.5
Cattle and sheep (upland: less favoured area)	27.0
Dairy	25.0
Mixed	3.0
Pigs and Poultry	2.0
Cereals, general cropping and horticulture	2.5
Other types	13.0
Livestock (x 1000)	
Cattle and calves (dairy cattle)	535 (132)
Sheep and lambs	2,700
Pigs	60
Poultry	1,800
Land designations and areas of conservation	
National Parks	Lakes District National Park Yorkshire Dales National Park (Part)
Sites of Special Scientific Interest[2]	230[3]
Special Areas of Conservation[2]	29
Special Protection Areas[2]	4
Environmentally Sensitive Areas	2[4]
Areas of Outstanding Natural Beauty[2]	3[5]
National Nature Reserves[2]	45
Local Nature Reserves[2]	6
County Wildlife Sites[2]	900

Notes: 1. Data based on the 1997 agricultural census and other sources.
2. Outside National Parks areas.
3. Approximate 178,500 ha.
4. Approximate 260,000 ha, including areas in the National Parks.
5. Approximate 78,800 ha; parts are in Lancashire, Northumberland and Durham.

Appendix 2. The Inquiry Panel and Secretariat

Inquiry Panel

Howard Christie FBII	Proprietor of the Wasdale Head Inn, Member of Wasdale Mountain Rescue Team and Chairman of Board of Haverigg Prison. Originally from a farming background; career in tourism in UK and abroad; former Manager of the Eskdale Outdoor Centre.
Jan Darrall BSc, PhD	Policy Officer with Friends of the Lake District and a Member of the Environmental Agency's North Area Environment Group and a Secretary of State Member of the Lake District National Park Authority. Background in research and policy studies in environment and the food chain, countryside leisure and environmental impact.
Professor Derek Ellwood BSc, PhD, FRSC, FIBiol	Retired Director of Westlakes Research Institute. Former Head of Biochemistry and Pathogenic Microbes, Porton Down and adviser to the United Nations and World Health Organisation. Current professorships at the Universities of Newcastle and Southampton.
David Etherden	Proprietor of tourism accommodation business and outdoor centre; Governor of Keswick School. Former Director of a Merchant Bank, with career in banking in the UK and overseas, before entering tourism industry.
Nick Gent MB,ChB, MSc, LLM, FFPHM	Specialist in infectious diseases, public health medicine, occupational medicine and environmental law. Former Director of Public Health for Morecambe Bay Health Authority and currently consultant in Health Protection in the UK and in the Balkans.
Philip Hancock	Feed and agricultural specialist. Partner in the feed supply business in Penrith. Background in agricultural supply industry; former career in supply management with the Unilever company.
John Hetherington BSc (Hons), NDA	Retired farmer with former career in agricultural education. Former Principal of Northumberland College of Agriculture; former Chairman of Harrison and Hetherington (livestock market), and Member of the Agricultural Land Tribunal. Personal experience of the 1958, 1967 and 2001 FMD epidemics.
Andrew Humphries NDA, MRAC, MPhil, FRAgS	Independent adviser on agriculture and rural affairs and a Member of the Government's Taskforce for the Hills; Chairman of the Rural Community Council. Former Assistant Director of Newton Rigg Agriculture College, Penrith; career in agricultural education and rural development.
Canon Geoffrey Ravalde Barrister at Law, BA, MA, MTh	Vicar of Wigton, after a previous period as Rural Dean of Carlisle and an earlier Ministry in rural Lincolnshire; Governor of Nelson Tomlinson Secondary School, Wigton. Former Barrister and Member of the Middle Temple.
Professor Phil Thomas BSc, PhD, CBiol, RNutr, FIBiol, FRAgS, FRSE (Chairman)	Food-chain consultant; Chairman of Animal Medicines Training Regulatory Authority and the Central Scotland Countryside Trust; Member of the Scottish Food Advisory Committee. Emeritus Professor of the Scottish Agricultural College (SAC) and Honorary Professor University of Edinburgh. Former Principal and Chief Executive of SAC, Professor of Agriculture of the University of Glasgow and member of UK and EU committees on nutrition.

Secretariat

John Hetherington	Environmental Partnerships Manager, Community, Economy and Environment
Jonathan Durnin	Senior Policy Officer, Policy and Performance
David Rackstraw	Solicitor (Legal Services)
Wendy Jones	Administration Officer
Suzannah Grindley	Administration Officer
Hamilton Tranter	Administration Officer
Sharon Swift	Administration Officer

Appendix 3. Contributors of written evidence.

Mr G. Ager	Environment Agency
Ms S. Aglionby	Carlisle
Ms J. Aglionby	H&H Bowe Ltd
Ms J. Airey	Keswick Tourism
Mr R.W. Almond	Isel, Cockermouth
Mr R. Armstrong	Penrith
Mr P. Ashcroft	Trading Standards
Ms R. Atkinson	Eden District Council
Mr W.M. Baty	Appleby Insurance Service
Mrs J. Baxter	Ulverston
Miss J. Bayley	National Foot and Mouth Group
Mr & Mrs A. Beat	Bridgerule, Devon
Mr A. Beeforth	Cumbria Community Foundation
Mr B. Bennison	Cumbria County Council
Mr R. C. Benson	Lowther Estates, Penrith
Mr H. Berger	The Burnmoor Inn
Dr S. Binns	Hockworthy
Mr D. Blunt	Great Orton
Mr P. Bonsall	Kirkby Stephen
Mr J. Boswell	Enterkine, Ayshire
Dr S. Bradley	Westlakes Research Institute
Ms K. Braithwaite	Voluntary Action Cumbria
Mr M.R. Bramley	Eden Farm Supplies, Shap
British Cattle Veterinary Association	
Mr G. Brown	Voluntary Action Cumbria
Prof N. Burrow	University of Central Lancashire, Carlisle
Mr J. Cain	Allerdale Borough Council
Mr G. Capstick	National Farmers Union
Mr D. Chalmers	Country Land and Business Association
Mr J. Chiyacklea	Ulverston
Mrs M. Clough	Bampton
Mr C.H. Cole	Cockermouth
Mrs C. Collier	Cumbria Tourist Board
Mr J. Cook	
Dr J. Cox	Northern Fells Rural Project
Dr S. Crispin	University of Bristol
Ms M. Critchley	
Mr D. Crummack	Sinnington, York
Mr K. De Vonald	Federation of Small Businesses
Mr B. P. Dennison	Spirit of Cumbria
Mr G.H. Dixon	Cartmel
Mr I. Dixon	Wigton
Mr J. Dixon	
Mr V. Dodd	Cumbria Chamber of Trade & Industry
Ms I.H. Dover	Keswick
Mr D. Dunlop	
Mr N. El-Far	Cockermouth
Mrs C. Elliot	
Mr M. Elliott	Cumbria County Council
Rev D. Emison	Churches Together in Cumbria
Mr V. Emmerson	Copeland Borough Council

Ms A. Eykyn	Foot and Mouth Disease Forum
Mr A. Fishwick	Lake District National Park
Mr C.R.A. Flanagan	The National Trust
Mrs C. Fletcher	Barwise Aberdeen Angus
Mr J. Foote	
Mr S. Gorman	Cumbria County Council
Mr P. Gray	East Cumbria Countryside Project
Mr N. Green	Heart of Cumbria
Mr S. Greenhalgh	Cumbria County Council
Ms S. Greenhill	Cockermouth
Mr P. Greenhill	Cockermouth
Mr T. Griffith-Jones	Skelmersdale, Lancashire
Mr M. Hancox	Stroud, Gloucestershire
Mr R. Hargreaves	Egremont
Mr H. Hawkins	Ramblers Association
Mr B. Hellier	Copeland Borough Council
Miss J. Hogg	Appleby Town Council
Mr C. Holmes	Carrs Milling PLC
Mr D. House	QIC Print, Carlisle
Mr J. Hunter	Aspatria Farmers
Lord W.R. Inglewood	House of Lords
Mr J. Jennings	Brougham
Mrs F. Johns	Langdale Leisure Ltd, Great Langdale
Mr K. Jones	Forestry Commission
Mr J. Jones	South Lakeland District Council
Dr S. Jones	
Mr P. Kidd	Longwathy
Mrs L.M. Kindleysides	Shap
Lakeland Veterinary Association	
Mrs C.A. Lambourn	Berkshire
Landscape Regeneration Group	Cumbria FMD Task Force
Mrs L. Layton	Seascale
Mr N.W. Leslie	Middlesborough
Mr W.E. Lett	Cockermouth
Mr M. Lewes	BBC Radio Cumbria
Mr B. Lightowler	Small Business Services
Mr W. Lloyd	Kendal
Mrs A. Logan	Spinneyside
Prof P. Lowe	C.R.E
Mr T. Lowther	Whitbysteads Hill Farm
Viscountess Lowther	Penrith
Mr M. MacInnes	Clark Scott-Harden, Penrith
Rt Hon D. Maclean	House of Commons
Mrs M. Marshall	Palmer & Marshall
Mr N. Mason	RSPB
Mr P. Messenger	Carlisle City Council
Mr K. Morgan	Appleby-in-Westmorland Town Council
Dr M. Mort	Lancaster University
Mrs K.W. Morton	Penrith
Mrs G. Moyle	National Association Citizens Advice Bureau
Mr H. Murray	Cumberland & Dumfriesshire Farmer's Mart P.L.C
National Foot and Mouth Group	
Mrs E.W. Nicholas	Kirkby Stephen
Mr D. Norrie	The Emergency Planning Society

Dr D. O'Halloran	English Nature
Ms H. O'Hare	Veterinary Surgeon
Mrs D. Owen	Cockermouth
Mr D. Parker	Longtown
Prof F. Peck	Northumbria University
Mr J. Peet	Jim Peet (Agriculture)
Mr A.A. Pickard	Sheffield
Mr G. Price	Bewcastle Parish Council
Mr J.M. Renshaw	Appleby-in-Westmorland
Mr A. Richardson	Penrith
Mrs R. Ridley	Kentmere
Mr P. Rooke	UKASTA
Mrs J. Rutherford	Messer Rutherford & Co
Ms V. Schofield	Carlisle
Mrs V. Simm	Stockport, Lancashire
Ms M. Sisson	Longtown
Mrs E. Skelton	Skelton Highgate and Animal Trail
Mr M. Smith	Cumbria County Council
Mr R. Speirs	Carlisle City Council
Cllr G. B. Strong	Midtown Farm
Mr J. Sutcliffe	Lowick, Ulverston
Mr K. Sutton	The Editor - Cumbrian Newspapers Ltd
Ms H. Tate	Cumbria Tourist Board
Mr & Mrs D. Taylor	Wigton
Mrs I.M. Thompson	Penrith
Mr P. Thompson	
Mr J. Thurgood	Heart of Cumbria
Dr P. Tiplady	North Cumbria Health Authority
Mr P. Tiplady	Lake District National Park
Mrs R. D. Turpling	Great Strickland Parish Council
Mrs T. Walker	Penrith
Mrs J. Walker	Cumbria Crisis Alliance
Mrs V. Waller	National Farmers Union
Mrs S.M. Walton	Kirkby Stephen
Mr D. Waugh	Youth Hostels Association
Ms D. Wilson	West Cumbria Development Agency
Mrs J.H. Wilson	Tebay
Mr R. S. Windsor	Dumfries
Mrs S. Wright	Farmers Weekly

Appendix 4. Inquiry Schedule.

PUBLIC HEARINGS

Kendal: 7 May 2002, morning
Presentations
Mr Keith Sutton   Cumberland News
Mr Gordon Swindlehurst   BBC Radio Cumbria
Brig Alex Birtwhistle   Former Army
Open Forum
Mr Tom Jones   UK Rural Business Campaign
Mr Roger Bingham   Chairman of South Lakeland District Council
Mr Geoffrey Dixon   Farmer, Cartmel Valley
Mr Geoffrey Swift   Farmer, Kendal

Kendal: 7 May 2002, afternoon
Presentations
Mrs Veronica Waller   National Farmers Union
Mr Steven Dunning   National Farmers Union
Mr William Cockbain   National Farmers Union
Mrs Suzanne Greenhill   Cockermouth
Open Forum
Mr Thomas Lowther   Farmer, Penrith
Mr Alastair McIntosh   Farmer, Ravenglass
Mr Norman Leslie   Veterinarian, Middlesborough

Kendal: 8 May 2002, morning
Presentations
Mr Nick Green   Heart of Cumbria
Mr Mick Elliot   Director of Safety Services, Cumbria County Council
Mr David Humphries   Emergency Planning Unit, Cumbria County Council
Mrs Lyndsay Cowan   Emergency Planning Unit, Cumbria County Council
Mr Geoff Brown   Herdwick Sheep Breeders' Association
Open Forum
Mrs Rosamund Ridley   Journalist, Kentmere

Kendal: 8 May 2002, afternoon
Presentations
Mr Ken De Vonald   Cumbria/Lancashire Federation of Small businesses
Miss Vivian Middleton   Cumbria/Lancashire Federation of Small businesses
Mr B. Lightowler   Business Link for Cumbria
Open Forum
Miss Jean Dixon   Campaign Against Culling
Mr T. Griffith-Jones   UK Rural Business Campaign

Kendal: 9 May 2002, morning
Presentations
Mrs Chris Collier   Cumbria Tourist Board
Mrs Jennifer Hogg   Tourist Information Centre, Appleby-in-Westmorland
Mr J. Walker   Cumbria Crisis Alliance

Kendal: 9 May 2002, afternoon
Presentations
Mrs Clare Edwards   Cumbria Community Foundation
Cllr Gary Strong   Farmer and County Councillor for Penrith Rural Division

Dr Jim Cox	Northern Fells Rural Project
Open Forum	
Cllr Philip Chappelhow	County Councillor, North Penrith and Lazonby

Kendal: 10 May 2002, morning
Presentations

Mr Nick Mason	The Royal Society for the Protection of Birds
Mr Charles Flanagan	Area Manager, National Trust
Mr Nick Hill	National Trust
Mr Paul Tiplady	Lake District National Park

Kendal: 10 May 2002, afternoon
Presentations

Dr. Peter Tiplady	Director of Public Health for North Health Cumbria
Mr. Ronald Hargreaves	Egremont
Mr. John Cook	Lakeland Veterinary Association

Carlisle: 28 May 2002, morning
Presentations

Mr John Cain	Environmental Health, Allerdale Borough Council
Mr John Dunning	North West Development Agency
Mr Ray Kessler	North West Development Agency
Mr Ian Bowness	Cumbria Cornerstone
Mrs Julia Aglionby	H&H Bowe, Chartered Surveyors

Carlisle: 28th May 2002, afternoon
Presentations

Lord Haskins	Former Government Rural Recovery Co-ordinator
Mr Nick Utting	National Farmers Union
Mr Les Armstrong	National Farmers Union
Miss Janet Bayley	National Foot and Mouth Group

Carlisle: 29 May 2002, morning
Presentations

Mr Stephen Greenhalgh	Restrictions Review Team, Cumbria Councty Council
Mr David Rackstraw	Legal Services, Cumbria County Council
Mr Rex Toft	Leader of Cumbria County Council
Mr Louis Victory	Chief Executive, Cumbria County Council
Open Forum	
Mrs Jane Krause	Cheshire County Council

Carlisle: 29 May 2002, afternoon
Presentations

Mr Philip Ashcroft	Trading Standards, Cumbria County Council
Mr Nick Middleton	Trading Standards, Cumbria County Council
Mr Paul Rooke	UKASTA
Professor Norman Burrows	University of Central Lancashire

Carlisle: 30 May 2002, morning
Presentations

Mrs Kate Braithwaite	Voluntary Action Cumbria
Mr Michael Hyatt	Policy and Performance, Cumbria County Council
Mr Graham McWilliam	Economic Development, Eden District Council
Mrs Catherine Elliot	Economic Development, Carlisle City Council
Open Forum	
Mr Harry Berger	Hotelier, Eskdale
Mrs Jaqueline Shepherd	Business proprietor, Eskdale

Carlisle. 30 May 2002, afternoon

Presentations

Miss Naomi Cohen	English Tourism Council
Professor Philip Lowe	Centre for Rural Economy, Newcastle University
Mr David Waugh	Youth Hostel Association
Mr Andy Auld	Citizens Advice Bureau, Carlisle

Open Forum

Mr. Philip Gray	East Cumbria Countryside Project
Mrs. Ellie Logan	Wigton

Carlisle: 31 May 2002, morning

Presentations

Mr John Pinder	Enviroment Agency
Dr Ian Lowles	Westlakes Research Institute
Mr David McLean	MP for Penrith

Open Forum

Mr Jullian Pellatt	Cheshire County Council
Mrs Gillian Forsythe	

Carlisle: 31 May 2002, afternoon

Presentations

Dr Maggie Mort	Institute for Health Research, Lancaster University
Professor Frank Peck	Institute for Health Research, Lancaster University
Rev David Emison	Churches Together in Cumbria

Forum

Mr Gordon Capstick	Former County Chairman, National Farmers Union
Dr Sheila Crispin	Veterinary Surgeon, University of Bristol
Mr Jim McCleland	County Chairman, National Farmers Union

MEETINGS

Windemere: 14 May 2002, morning

Environmental Issues

Mr Bob Cartwirght	Lake District National Park Authority
Mr Nicholas Hill	National Trust
Mr Ian Brodie	Friends of Lake District
Mr Keith Jones	Forestry Commission
Ms Kathryn Beardmore	Yorkshire Dales National Park Authority
Mr Jeff Birkbeck	Swaledale Sheep Association
Mr Steve Dunning	National Farmers Union
Mr Gilbert Tyson	Herdwick Sheep Association

Windemere: 14 May 2002, afternoon

Access issues

Mr Keith Jones	Forestry Commission
Mr Bob Cartwright	LDNPA
Mr Syd McLennan	Sedbergh Footpath Action Group
Mr Ian Brodie	Friends of Lake District
Mr David Waugh	YHA
Mr Harry Hawkins	Ramblers Association
Mr Peter Jones	Ramblers Association
Mrs Kathryn Beardmore	YDNPA
Mr David Rackstraw	Cumbria County Council

Moota, near Cockermouth; 15 May 2002, morning

Community Health issues

Mrs Clare Edwards	Cumbria Community Foundation
Mr David Andrews	Cumbria Community Foundation
Mrs Jane Sharpe	Scott Trusts
Mr Mike Graham	Carlisle Primary Care Trust
Mrs Alison Phillips	Voluntary Action Cumbria
Mrs Debbie Steele	Voluntary Action Cumbria
Mrs Alison Marrs	Voluntary Action Cumbria
Mrs Marianne Teasdale	Voluntary Action Cumbria
Mrs Sue Mallin	Eden Valley Primary Care Trust
Mrs Sue Black	Eden Valley Primary Care Trust
Dr Peter Tiplady	Cumbria/Lancs Health Authority

Newton Rigg College, Penrith: 15 May 2002, afternoon

Business issues

Mr Richard B. Allen	Tourism operator
Mr John Walker	Cumbria Crisis Alliance
Mr John Rushton	Cumbria Crisis Alliance
Mr W. Pearson	Cumbria Crisis Alliance
Mr Ian Friel	Barclays Bank
Mr Brian Lightowler	Business Link for Cumbria
Mrs Chris Collier	Cumbria Tourist Board

Longtown Market: 16 May 2002

Animal Movement

Mr Thomas Armstrong	Chairman, Longtown Market
Mr Haigh Murray	Auctioneer, Longtown Market

Carlisle, 16 May 2002

Business issues

Mrs J. Whyberd	William Armstrong
Mr Andrew Wright	Auctioneers Association
Mr Viv Dodd	Cumbria Chamber of Commerce

Carlisle: 30 May 2002

Contingency Planning

Mr Donald Norrie	Cumbria County Council
Mr David Humphries	Cumbria County Council

Carlisle: 5 June 2002

Veterinary issues

Mr Richard Sibley	British Cattle Veterinary Association

Carlisle: 11 June 2002

Future of Farming

Sir Don Curry	Commission on the Future of Food and Farming
Various	Members of the Cumbria Rural Action Zone Steering Group

COMMUNITY MEETINGS

Workington: 13 May 2002
Ulverston : 14 May 2002
Appleby: 15 May 2002

Longtown: 16 May 2002
Great Orton: 28 May 2002
Grasmere: 12 June 2002

SITE VISITS

Longtown Market: 16 May 2002
Watchtree Burial Site: 16 May 2002
Distington Landfill: 16 May 2002

Appendix 5. Distribution of Foot and Mouth infected premises in Britain (provided by DEFRA 2002).

22/10/2001

Appendix 6. Some aspects of the 1967-68 epidemic and the 2001 epidemic.

	1967-68 Epidemic	2001 Epidemic
Suspected source of virus	Imported frozen lamb from Argentina	Infected illegally imported meat from Far East
Speed of identification of source case	Four days	Approximately 3 weeks
Extent of initial seeding of cases	Twenty-four almost simultaneous outbreaks	At least 57 premises in 16 Counties
Extent of disease spread	Confined mainly to the Cheshire Plain, but including Cheshire, Staffordshire, Montgomeryshire, Denbighshire, Shropshire and Flintshire	Widely distributed in 44 British counties, unitary authorities and metropolitan districts from the Scottish Borders to Anglesey to Cornwall
Cause of spread	Mainly airborne	Initially movements of infected animals. Later local spread from initial sources of infection
Total number of infected premises	2,364	2,026
Duration of epidemic	222 days	221 days
Numbers of vets mobilised	645	1,800
Time before military directly involved	12 days	25 days
Number of troops deployed	400	More than 2,000.
Numbers of animals slaughtered	442,000 (49% cattle, 26% pigs and 25% sheep)	Approximately 4,200,000 (12% cattle, 3% pigs and 85% sheep)

Appendix 7. Distribution of Foot and Mouth Disease in Cumbria. Data for the whole epidemic showing infected premises and 3km zones (provided by DEFRA 2002.)

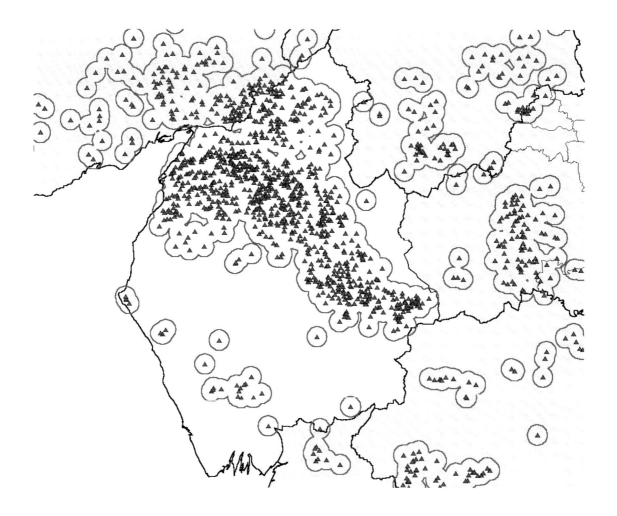

Appendix 8. Progression of the Foot and Mouth Disease epidemic in Cumbria.

1 March 2001

14 March 2001

28 March 2001

11 April 2001

23 April 2001

7 May 2001

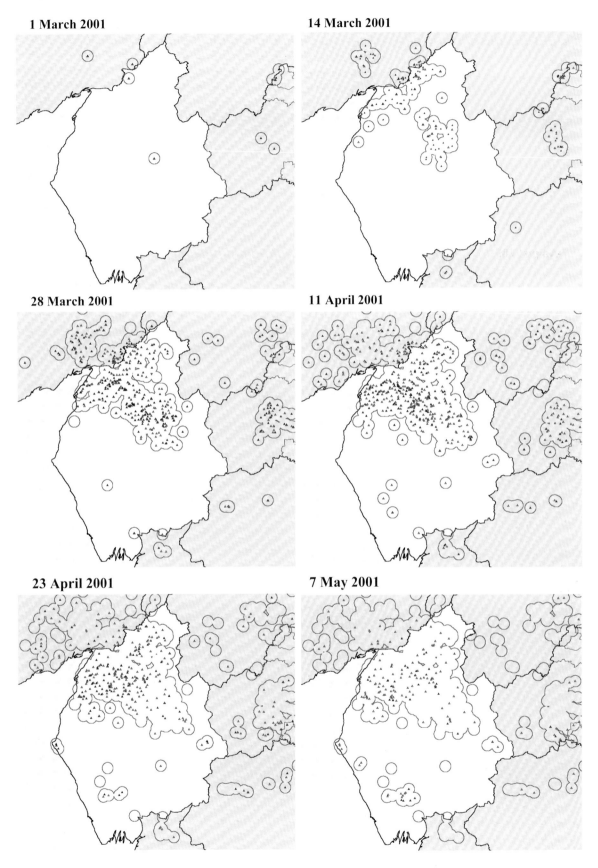

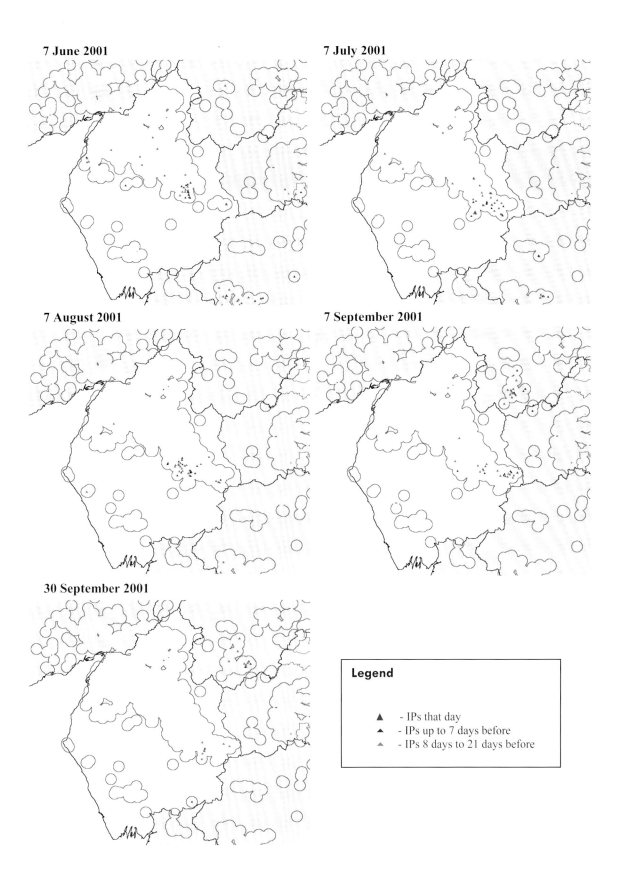

7 June 2001

7 July 2001

7 August 2001

7 September 2001

30 September 2001

Legend

▲ - IPs that day
▲ - IPs up to 7 days before
▲ - IPs 8 days to 21 days before

Appendix 9. Outline map of Cumbria showing Districts and National Parks.

Appendix 10. Outline map of Cumbria showing key places referred to in this report.

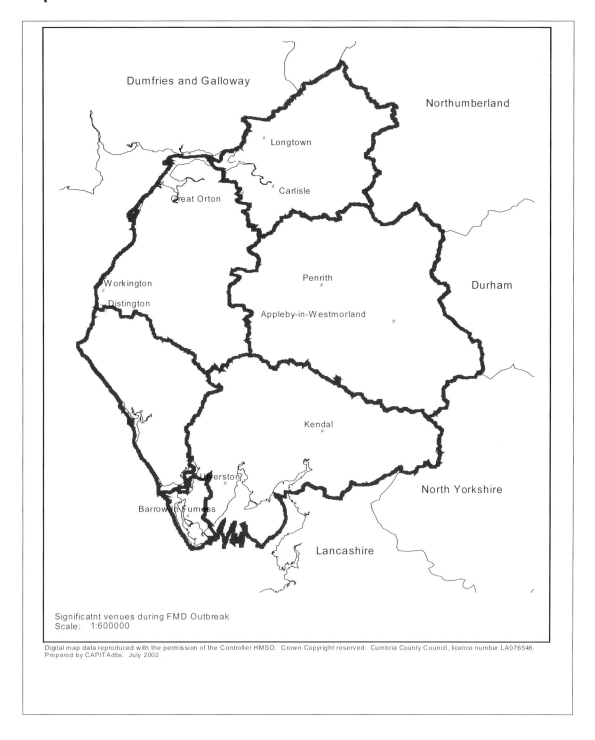

GLOSSARY

Animal Health Office	Regional Office of the SVS
AONB	Areas of Outstanding Natural Beauty
BBC	British Broadcasting Council
BSE	Bovine Spongiform Encephalopathy
CAB	Citizen's Advice Bureau
CAP	Common Agricultural Policy of the EU
COBR	Cabinet Office Briefing Room
Controlled area	Area of designated FMD control measures operate
CRE	Centre for Rural Economy
CSA	Chief Scientific Adviser
CTB	Cumbria Tourist Board
CVO	Chief Veterinary Officer
DCC	Disease Control Centre
DECC	Departmental Emergency Control Centre
DEFRA	Department of Environment, Food and Rural Affairs
DETR	Department of Environment, Transport and the Regions
DNA	Deoxyribonucleic acid
DoH	Department of Health
EC	European Commission
ELISA	Enzyme-linked Immunosorbent Assay
ERDP	European Regional Development Programme
ESA	Environmentally Sensitive Area
EU	European Union
FE	Further Education
FSA	Food Standards Agency
FMD	Foot and Mouth Disease
GDP	Gross Domestic Product
Great Britain	England, Wales and Scotland
HE	Higher Education
Heafed sheep	Hefted sheep – sheep habituated to an open grazing area
ICT	Information and Computing Technology
IP	Infected Premises
JCC	Joint Control Centre
LDNPA	Lake District National Park Authority
Leader+	European Union Leader Programme
Local Authority	Local Government Body
LSCs	Learning and Skills Councils
M6	The M6 Motorway
MAFF	Ministry of Agriculture Fisheries and Food
NAO	National Audit Office
NFU	National Farmers Union
NWDA	North West Development Agency
MP	Member of Parliament
MEP	Member of European Parliament
OIE	Office International des Epizooties
PAH	Polyaromatic hydrocarbon
PCB	Polychlorinated biphenyl
'Penrith Spur'	Area of Cumbria around Penrith
RAZ	Rural Action Zone
Restricted Infected Area	Designated area in which biosecurity measures are imposed
RNA	Ribonucleic acid
Royal Society	The Royal Society of London

Royal Society of Edinburgh	The Royal Society of Edinburgh
RSPCA	Royal Society for the Prevention of Cruelty to Animals
RT-PCR	Reverse Transcriptase-Polymerase Chain Reaction
SEAC	Spongiform Encepthalopathy Advisory Committee
SBS	Small Business Service
SO	Strategic Objective in the RAZ programme
State Aid Rules	EU rules governing industry aid in Member States
SVS	State Veterinary Service
UK	United Kingdom of Great Britain and Northern Ireland
USDA	United States Department of Agriculture
VAT	Value Added Tax
YDNPA	Yorkshire Dales National Park Authority
YHA	Youth Hostel Association

NOTES

[1] We have used the term 'epidemic' to describe the large-scale occurrence of FMD in parts of UK in 2001. Since the disease was not endemic in the country, it would technically more correct to use the term 'outbreak'. However, we have adopted the colloquial use of 'epidemic' as an 'outbreak of epidemic proportions'. We have used 'outbreak' in the context of a farm or cluster of farms affected by FMD e.g. a new outbreak.

[2] The number of FMD outbreaks reported for Cumbria varies slightly depending on the data source from 891 to 894. These differences relate mainly to instances where an outbreak lay on the edge of the County and was dealt with by a Disease Control Centre other than Carlisle; thus affecting its recording in the DEFRA statistics. In the report we have used the figures supplied in data sets by DEFRA or other official sources.

[3] This approach also avoids confusion in situations where DEFRA documents are referring to events before the 8 June.

[4] Oral evidence from Keith Sutton, Brigadier Alex Birtwhistle and Peter Tiplady.

[5] The Anderson Inquiry was published 22 July 2002. See, Anderson, I. (2002) *Foot and Mouth Disease 2001: Lessons to be Learned Inquiry Report*. The Stationery Office, London.

[6] The Royal Society Report was published on the 18 July 2002. See, Royal Society (2002) *Infectious Diseases in Livestock*. Royal Society, London. (www.royalsoc.ac.uk).

[7] Policy Commission on Food and Farming (2002) *Food and Farming a Sustainable Future*. (www.cabinet-office.gov.uk/farming).

[8] Agriculture Strategy Steering Group (2001) *A Forward Strategy for Scottish Agriculture*. (www.scotland.gov.uk/publications).

[9] The Government of the National Assembly for Wales (2001) *A New Direction for Farming in Wales*. (www.wales.gov.uk/subiagriculture/content/futures/futuresgroup_e.htm).

[10] It should be noted that, although a major area of livestock production, Cumbria had been free from FMD for half a century and although affected by outbreaks in other parts of the UK has no history as an area in which FMD has arisen.

[11] DEFRA (2001) Comments to Local Inquiries. (www.defra.gov.uk/corporate/inquiries/index.asp)

[12] Local public inquiries have been organised by the Devon and Northumberland County Councils, investigations have been undertaken by the Shropshire and Gloucestershire County Councils. An inquiry in Scotland undertaken by the Royal Society of Edinburgh was published on 16 July 2002. These documents provide a more detailed insight into events and experiences in some other parts of Great Britain.

[13] Government Memorandum Addressing the Issues Raised in the Framework Document of the Lessons Learned Inquiry (2002) (www.defra.gov.uk/corporate/inquiries/index.asp).

[14] European Parliament Temporary Committee on Foot and Mouth (2002) *Answers to questions to UK Government representatives and former representatives for the meeting of*

the European Parliament Temporary Committee on Foot and Mouth Disease 26 March and 8 April 2002. (www.defra.gov.uk/corporate/inquiries/index.asp).

[15] National Audit Office (2002) *The 2001 Outbreak of Foot and Mouth Disease*, Report by the Comptroller and Auditor General. The Stationery Office, London.

[16] DEFRA (2002) *Origin of the UK Foot and Mouth Disease Epidemic 2001.* (www.defra.gov.uk/corporate/inquiries/index.asp).

[17] Janet Bayley drew our attention to the fact that the EU FMD Conference on the 30-31 March 2000 had made the following statement. 'The commission noted the deteriorating FMD situation in Asia and recommends that all member countries should learn from the recent experience of Japan and Korea and strengthen and heighten their preparedness and awareness of the risks of FMD.'

[18] European Commission (2001) *Final Report of a Mission Carried Out in the United Kingdom from 12-16 March in Order to Evaluate the Situation with Regard to Outbreaks of Foot and Mouth Disease.* DG(SANCO)/3318/2001 – MR final.
European Commission (2001) *Final Report of a Mission Carried Out in the United Kingdom from 23-27 April in Order to Evaluate the Situation with Regard to Outbreaks of Foot and Mouth Disease.* DG(SANCO)/3328/2001 – MR final.
European Commission (2001) *Final Report of a Mission Carried Out in the United Kingdom (Northern Ireland) from 30 April – 4 May in Order to Evaluate the Situation with Regard to Outbreaks of Foot and Mouth Disease.* DG(SANCO)/3331/2001 – MR Final.
European Commission (2001) *Final Report of a Mission Carried Out in the United Kingdom from 20-24 August in Order to Evaluate the Situation with Regard to Outbreaks of Foot and Mouth Disease.* DG(SANCO)/3439/2001 – MR final.
(See http://europa.eu.int/comm/food/fs/inspections/index_en.html).

[19] The FMD Contingency Plans for Great Britain were updated in July 2000.

[20] Departments and others represented at COBR were: Number 10; Cabinet Office; Ministry of Defence; HM Treasury; MAFF (later DEFRA); Department of Environment, Transport and the Regions (later DEFRA); Department of Culture, Media and Sport; Department of Education and Employment (later Department for Work and Pensions); Department of Transport, Local Government and the Regions; Department of Health; Home Office; Department of Trade and Industry; Office of Science and Technology; Foreign and Commonwealth Office; Regional Co-ordination Unit; Inland Revenue; Environment Agency; Food Standards Agency; Scottish Executive; National Assembly of Wales.

[21] The BSE Inquiry (2000) Volume 1: *Findings and Conclusions.* The Stationery Office, London.

[22] Epidemiologists were from teams at three universities (Imperial College, Cambridge and Edinburgh) and the Veterinary Laboratory Agency.

[23] Biosecurity was a term that very much 'emerged' during the course of the epidemic. It still suffers from a lack of precise definition in regard to the most effective measures to apply in reducing the risk of spread of FMD.

[24] 'Dirty vets' referred to vets who had visited infected farms and who, as a consequence, presented a risk of spreading disease. The livestock valuation process had become problematic because it was claimed to be slowing down the authorisation of slaughter.

[25] There was concern over the backlog of animals waiting slaughter and disposal. Also that the epidemic would 'break out' of Cumbria and spread to clean areas of the country further south. As indicated later the 'fire break' approach around Cumbria was apparently not implemented.

[26] Sheep, which are behaviourally bonded to particular areas of unfenced land, are known as hefted flocks in most parts of the UK. In Cumbria they are locally described as heafed, and are part of a land management heritage of grazing unrestricted Fells forming Common Land.

[27] National Audit Office (2002) *The 2001 Outbreak of Foot and Mouth Disease*, Report by the Comptroller and Auditor General. The Stationery Office, London.

[28] Figures calculated from data supplied by DEFRA.

[29] For example, Anthrax and Rabies would come into these categories.

[30] This is discussed more fully in Part 3 of the report.

[31] Louis Victory, Chief Executive of Cumbria County Council, and Mick Elliot, Director of Safety Services, told us that there was an early consideration of what was thought would be required and whether the County's Emergency Centre should be opened. However, there was a clear view that MAFF was the body with the expertise and remit to lead in the area of animal diseases.

[32] In the early part of the epidemic agricultural suppliers and others were frustrated that DEFRA was refusing to disclose information about the location of FMD outbreaks other than the basis of Parish and District. This policy originated from the instructions in *Veterinary Instructions, Procedures and Emergency Routines*, which restrict disclosure of further information to police, local authorities and milk companies. During the epidemic this restriction was abandoned.

[33] From our public meetings it was apparent that members of the public had made representations to MPs and MEPs about what was happening in Cumbria. However, there was a sense that those who were responsible for the FMD eradication programme were not listening to the voices of the community. In evidence, we were made aware of personal correspondence between David Maclean MP and the Prime Minister highlighting the dire nature of the problems being encountered in Cumbria and urging that something should be done to alleviate the situation.

[34] Many people described events as being chaotic. It was difficult for farmers to maintain a clear view of the policy from week to week. Often there was a perception that two policies were operating at the same time (which it appears may actually have been the case). Key stages of the epidemic at which the Government could have used the media to advantage to provide a sense of clear purpose were missed.

[35] We were unable to question DEFRA staff, but the implication of this situation is that communication within DEFRA was also ineffective and that those who were dealing with the public were not provided with adequate information.

[36] We received numerous accounts from farmers of DEFRA field staff having difficulty obtaining up to date information. By DEFRA's own account there appear to have been instances when there was a significant time delay between the announcement of a policy change in the disease control system and the detail of the change being provided in writing to the field operatives.

[37] An illustrative case was the approach taken to the implementation of the voluntary 3km-zone cull of sheep. The following is an actually example.

Background On 6 March 2001 Farm A near Dearham was confirmed as having FMD. The sheep at the premises were slaughtered and the carcasses burnt on 10 March. On the 29 March Farm B, within the 3km zone, was contacted by Harrison and Hetherington, acting on behalf of MAFF to inquire whether they would 'let their sheep go' under the voluntary cull. The farmer declined the offer on the basis that, in over three weeks, there had been no further FMD cases in the area, that their sheep were fully healthy and that their cattle, which were housed with the sheep, were also healthy. Two weeks later still, on the 13 April 2001, with the 3km zone still having no new FMD outbreaks Farm B received the following letter from MAFF.

'Dear -----

In March the Minister for Agriculture announced that all sheep in the 3km zones around an infected premises in certain areas of Cumbria must be slaughtered. This was following the advice of the Chief Veterinary Officer and MAFF's scientific advisors who believe that sheep within these zones will have been exposed to infection. They also believe that by slaughtering these sheep the impact of the spread of disease will be reduced.

Following consultation with members of the NFU a decision was made to remove sheep from farms in the 3km zones to a central place for slaughter. This gave farmers the opportunity to avoid the slaughter of sheep on their own premises and enabled the slaughter of about 20,000 sheep a day without impacting heavily on the available resources. To this end local auction marts contacted farmers in the 3km zones and invited them to give up their sheep. Arrangements were then made for sheep to be valued, collected and slaughtered.

According to our records you were not willing to give up your sheep. This letter is to advise you what arrangements are now being put in place to include your sheep in the cull.

In the infected area, sheep, goats and pigs on premises within 3km of an infected premises will be treated as Dangerous Contacts. This means that the Ministry of Agriculture will make arrangements for your sheep to be slaughtered on the farm. Compensation will be paid for your sheep.

If you have reason to believe that your flock has not been exposed to infection it may be possible to arrange for them to be subjected to repeated serological surveillance to confirm your beliefs. You will need to contact your local veterinary surgeon and ask him, at your expense, to visit your flock and make a submission to the Senior Veterinary Officer at Hadrian House Carlisle. He will need to include in his submission arguments why your flock, or part of it, should be exempt from the cull. He will need to prove that they have been isolated from other stock and high levels of biosecurity have been sustained since the end of February. These cases will be referred to MAFF Head Office.

If rather than have your sheep slaughtered on farm you would like to have them taken away for slaughtering please phone 01228 590490 and ask for Mark Lawson or Michael Armstrong. They will arrange for your sheep to be valued and transported to Great Orton or Carlisle Abattoir for slaughtering.

Yours sincerely'

[38] We can make no judgement in these cases of dispute whether DEFRA or the farmers involved are in the right. However, confirmation of instructions by letter would be regarded as good practice.

[39] This is the conclusion presented in the Anderson Committee Report, although the account the CVO's report is less clear on the point. There were markets at Longtown on the 15 February and on the 22 February and the first reported FMD case in Cumbria was on the 28 February. The incubation period of the disease is under 5 days so that it seems technically possible that the disease could have spread from Longtown on either the 15 February or the 22 February. However, if the earlier date applies, the disease was unnoticed in Cumbria for 10-12 days.

[40] Information from the Government's submission to the Anderson Inquiry.

[41] Data taken from NAO (2002). Outbreak figures of 891 quoted for Cumbria are as reported.

[42] DEFRA (2002) *Origin of the UK Foot and Mouth Disease Epidemic 2001.* (www.defra.gov.uk/corporate/inquiries/index.asp).

[43] Figures calculated from data supplied to the Inquiry by DEFRA. Total cases, which had been investigated, were 1,069 for Cumbria and are higher than the number of confirmed cases reported in other data sets. Figures shown exclude 55 cases in Cumbria and 143 elsewhere, reported as still under investigation.

[44] Evidence provided by H. Murray of Longtown Market.

[45] The cost of upkeep of road mats was high. On the limited scale undertaken by the County Council the disinfectant and labour costs were £50k per week, not taking into account the opportunity cost of diverting staff from other work.

[46] Northumberland, Lord (1969) *Report of the Committee of Inquiry on Foot and Mouth Disease.* Volume 1 (Cmnd. 3999) and Volume 2 (Cmnd. 4225). Her Majesty's Stationery Office, London.

[47] A letter from the Minister to the Chief Executive of the Council at the end of March indicated that mats were of little use but further consultation with the DECC elicited different guidance.

[48] Oral evidence from Jennifer Whyberd.

[49] Ellard, F. M., Drew, J., Blakemore, W. E., Stuart, D. I. and King, A. M. Q.(1999) *Evidence for the role of His-142 of protein 1C in the acid-induced disassembly of foot-and-mouth disease virus capsids.* Journal of General Microbiology 80, 1911-1918.

[50] Evidence provided at the Public Meeting in Appleby.

[51] One of the conclusions of this report was that 'The initial reluctance to consider preventative slaughter of 'at risk' holdings (within 1km of an infected premises) is likely to have delayed the eradication of the disease, and has risked its spread to neighbouring holdings in some areas.' One of the recommendations of the report is 'Consider preventative slaughter in certain circumstances in an attempt to get ahead of the disease, and to reduce the weight of infection to which animals are exposed.'

[52] DEFRA (2002) *Report of the Committee of Inquiry on Foot and Mouth Disease 1967-68: Applicability of Recommendations during the 2001 Outbreak.* (www.defra.gov.uk/corporate/inquiries/index.asp).

[53] The written responses to the questions asked do not give precise figures to the hour. We have therefore taken the indicative figures expressed in days as an indicator of events.

[54] The key controls for ensuring humane slaughter in accordance with the Welfare of Animals (Slaughter and Killing) Regulations 1995 were: use of only licensed slaughtermen and audit of slaughter arrangements by DEFRA vets, who were also responsible for killing young animals by lethal injection.

[55] For example, written and oral evidence from Nick Green, Ellie Logan and received during public meetings.

[56] The information given here is taken from Part 3 of the Report of the Comptroller and Auditor General (2002).

[57] Although these figures are not precise they indicate that during the March and April period of the epidemic the time from slaughter to disposal was much longer than indicated by the average UK figures for the epidemic as a whole.

[58] We received a personal account of this kind of situation in oral evidence from Councillor G. Strong whose 246 cattle and 750 sheep had been disposed of a week after slaughter. By that time the animals were beginning to decompose and 'come apart' as they were being moved for destruction. This was a 'great indignity to the animals' and the smell was causing significant distress both to the farmer and his family and to his neighbours in the nearby village.

[59] Written evidence from G. Ager, Environment Agency.

[60] Examples were given in the oral and written evidence from Nick Green and Ellie Logan.

[61] Examples were given in the oral and written evidence of Nick Green and in evidence we received during public meetings.

[62] Written evidence from G. Ager, Environment Agency.

[63] Oral evidence from John Cain, Allerdale District Council and in evidence we received during public meetings.

[64] Data has been calculated from information published on the DEFRA Internet site.

[65] DEFRA (2002) *Illegal Imports of Animal and Plant Products: DEFRA Action Plan 2002-03*. (www.defra.gov.uk/animalh/int-trde/prod-im/prod-im.htm).

[66] See DEFRA (2002) *Protecting Our Livestock and Plants from Pests and Disease*. New initiatives were announced by the Government on 8 July 2002.

[67] Figures are taken from DEFRA (2002) *Report of the Committee of Inquiry on Foot and Mouth Disease 1967-68: Applicability of Recommendations during the 2001 Outbreak*.

[68] The NAO report indicates that only 5% of contiguous premises were submitted for laboratory analysis and of these 30% were positive for FMD and 70% were negative. However, the samples submitted were not a random sample of the contiguous premises culled. Samples for laboratory analysis would be more likely to be submitted in cases where there was some clinical reason for suspecting that the premises was an undiagnosed infected premises. Therefore the 30% figure is likely to have a 'high' bias.

[69] We were told in the evidence of William Cockbain of the NFU that, at a stakeholder meeting, DEFRA had stated that a sub-sample of some 5,800 sheep from 115 farms slaughtered and buried at the Watchtree disposal site had been tested for FMD. It was said that only one farm had tested positive and there were three farms that were inconclusive. However, these figures are consistent with a policy of transferring non-infected but 'at risk' animals to the central slaughter and disposal site.

[70] Regulations derive from Commission Decision 2001/257/EC.

[71] Sales of unpasteurised milk are legally permitted in England and Wales, although not in Scotland.

[72] It appears that there is a provision to avoid this constraint 'under exceptional circumstances' but it is not clear what circumstances might be considered exceptional.

[73] A number of oral and written submissions of evidence included detailed considerations of aspects of the use of vaccination in FMD prevention and/or control. These included contributions from Suzanne Greenhill, Julia Aglionby, Janet Bayley and Sheila Crispin.

[74] It is now possible, using DNA technologies, to produce proteins associated with the virulence of the FMD virus. This technically will allow a single vaccine to be produced that would be effective against all serotypes.

[75] The opening of the Emergency Centre was a key factor in the multi-agency response to FMD that occurred in Dumfries and Galloway in 2001.

[76] According to the written statement of Dr Roger Breeze of the USDA made to the Royal Society Inquiry, this technology was offered to the Pirbright Laboratory in the UK for evaluation in 2001. However, the laboratory was apparently fully committed in dealing with the ongoing UK epidemic; the offer was therefore not taken up. Pirbright is also developing a RT-PCR test system.

[77] We received a range of submissions and comments concerning the ethical, moral and legal arguments against a policy that involved the slaughter of healthy animals not infected with FMD. These arguments have merits. However, even from the standpoint of resource use in implementing an efficient control and eradication policy, there is a case for minimising unnecessary animal slaughter and disposal.

[78] In Local Authorities the appointees would generally be Trading Standards Officers.

[79] During the Inquiry such organisations as the Environment Agency and the Allerdale Borough Council Environmental Health Department mentioned to us their arrangements for keeping off land as a precaution against spreading the virus.

[80] Later there was some contrary local public reaction over the continued denial of footpath access and a threat of a 'mass trespass' at Dunmail Raise.

[81] In their submission Stephen Greenhalgh (Assistant Director, Area Support) and David Rackstraw (County Council Solicitor) said that there was 'great pressure and advice to close or severely limit access to the countryside'.

[82] Other local authorities made similar declarations, including Durham and Northumberland on 28 February and Lancashire at the beginning of March.

[83] Most public and private organisations closed a wide range of visitor sites, car parks and lay-byes believing that this would help to stop the spread of the disease. The risk assessments were produced to help owners of a variety of sites to decide whether or not they could safely open their location. The sites that were reopened were therefore not simply Rights of Way or permissive paths.

[84] In October a grant from the Countryside Agency allowed the establishment of what was called the Footpath Access Team. This team dealt with many of the issues of path opening as

well as the digitisation of footpath maps for the County. At the height of activities the Footpath Access Team numbered 9 staff. Additionally, for much of the period of opening four Officers of the Trading Standards Department were required to deal with paths for which individual closure orders were needed where the areas closures had been lifted.

[85] The guidance note was subsequently updated on a regular basis as the epidemic progressed.

[86] Ben Gill is the President of the National Farmers Union.

[87] Oral evidence presented by Naomi Cohen.

[88] The District figures mask significant variations in employment levels from place to place within a District. Much of the employment in Cumbria is 'local', although there is some longer-distance travel to work where the main road communications are good. This includes some West to East travel in the northern part of the County.

[89] Figures are taken from Pion Economics (2002) *Economic Impact of FMD in North West England*, supplied by Cumbria County Council.

[90] This is the official Treasury estimate.

[91] Data adapted from the DTZ Pieda Report (2001) *Economic Impacts of Foot and Mouth Disease on the Cumbrian Economy.*

[92] There was evidence of this in some of the industry survey data supplied by the Cumbria Tourist Board, which reported that 31% of businesses cut back on recruitment of summer staff and 26% reduced staff hours.

[93] See DEFRA (2002) *England's Rural Future.* This paper sets out the Government's approach to re-launching the countryside, for extending the package of short-term help for affected businesses and for easing the restrictions on restocking of farms. (www.defra.gov.uk/corporate/publications/pubcat/rural.htm).

[94] Two new funds have been introduced recently. The Rural Renewal Fund (£3m), managed by the Small Business Service is an initiative by the Department for Trade and Industry to help FMD-affected business communities to revive their fortunes. The Countryside Access Fund (£0.5) is to assist voluntary bodies who were affected by restrictions on access to the countryside. It is administered through the Countryside Agency. These funds were not operating in the main period of time the Inquiry investigated and have therefore not been considered.

[95] The Cumbrian scheme allowed for eligible businesses to receive £2,000 for computing, up to £6,000 for marketing and £7,500 for interest relief. In October 2001 the scheme was extended to allow interest relief for business that had an existing commercial mortgage.

[96] The Steering Group membership comprised: Allerdale Borough Council; Carlisle City Council; Copeland Borough Council; Cumbria Chamber of Commerce; Cumbria County Council; Cumbria Crisis Alliance; Cumbria Tourist Board; DEFRA; Eden District Council; Government Office North West; Lake District National Park; Learning and Skills Council; National Farmers Union; North Cumbria Health Authority; North West Development Agency; Small Business Service; South Lakeland District Council; The National Trust; Voluntary Action Cumbria.

[97] For example, the Cumbria Tourist Board offered businesses a survival toolkit, developed by Lamont Pridmore, to assist in the prioritisation of key business decisions arising from the market collapse.

[98] NWDA set up a FMD rural survival fund in March. This was increased to £2m, with £1.5m allocated to Cumbria. Its Rural Renaissance (Regional Rural Recovery Plan) indicates its commitment to a programme of £100m in a Regional Rural Recovery Plan total of £398m over 5years: 67% of this allocation is to Cumbria.

[99] The logic of the funding allocations was difficult to understand. In the parts of the country affected by FMD, British tourists comprise some 80% of the visitors. Logic therefore suggests that the greater proportion of the funding available should have been directed through the English Tourism Council rather than the British Tourist Authority, as was the case. There was suspicion amongst tourism operators that the funding announcements may have involved some re-presentation of existing funding allocations and a pattern of spend directed at city tourism rather than rural tourism.

[100] The scheme operated under the *de minimus* provisions of the State Aid Rules which allow assistance of up to E100k over three years, except in the case of agriculture where no *de minimus* provision applies.

[101] Environment Agency (2001) *The Environmental Impact of the Foot and Mouth Disease Outbreak: An Interim Assessment.* Environment Agency, Bristol. (www.environment-agency.gov.uk).

[102] This Act forms part of the regime for BSE control.

[103] This Action Plan has been endorsed by a wide range of bodies. These include: Arnside/Silverdale Area of Outstanding Natural Beauty; The Countryside Agency; Cumbria County Council; Cumbria Landscape Project; Cumbria Wildlife Trust; East Cumbria Countryside Project; English Nature; Forestry Commission; Friends of the Lake District; Lake District National Park Authority; The National Trust; and Solway Coast Area of Outstanding Natural Beauty.

[104] There was also evidence that the lack of farm profitability and the clean-up processes that had been applied during the FMD epidemic had resulted in an adverse effect on Cumbria's built heritage. A report prepared by Mr P Messenger of Carlisle City Council contained evidence of the poor state of repair of many vernacular buildings and of damage as a result of FMD operations.

[105] These sites are all operated by Cumbria Waste Management Ltd.

[106] This site is operated by Alco Waste Management Ltd.

[107] Ash was disposed of either by burial or landfill. Of the 130 pyres ash was buried at 64 and removed to commercial landfill at 66.

[108] Some confidence in this was later gained from a study Assessment *of Risk due to BSE Infectivity from Burning Cattle due to FMD* (March 2000) by DNV Consulting which was obtained from MAFF.

[109] Data from Kate Bennett and Jeremy Franks (2002) The effects on farming life in the Northern Fells. In *Coping with Crisis in Cumbria: the Consequences of Foot and Mouth Disease.* Centre for Rural Economy, University of Newcastle upon Tyne.

[110] Organisations included: Voluntary Action Cumbria; Citizens Advice Bureau; Cumbria Community Foundation; Council for Agriculture and Rural Life; the Rural Stress Information Network; the Churches and many more.

[111] This fund was launched in April 2001 and raised over £2.1m. Major sources of funding were: the NWDA (£800k); Cumbria County Council (£52k); Charitable Trust funds (£360k); Countryside Agency (£430k); and individual donations (£500k).

[112] In his submission of evidence Mr Andy Beeforth, the Director of the Cumbria Community Foundation indicated that some 370 grant applications had been received from voluntary and community groups, suggesting that there were financial pressures still to be addressed. He indicated that the Foundation was seeking to establish grant programmes for the medium-term with funding through the Rural Action Zone programme.

[113] This recommendation should be considered in conjunction with the establishment of Access Fora under the Countryside and Rights of Way Act. The Restrictions Review Team had considerable success in achieving a constructive dialogue between land managers and other stakeholders and efforts should be made to build on the understanding and rapport that has been established.

[114] In his oral evidence Michael Hyatt of Cumbria County Council highlighted the difficulties of bringing together the 'visionaries' and 'pragmatists' necessary firstly to conceive a leading edge programme and secondly to develop the funding streams and operating systems necessary for the delivery of the programme 'on the ground'. His view was that the way that regeneration funding was conventionally structured mitigated against the sustained engagement of the 'visionaries'. He thus consider the next phase of the RAZ development, including the development of the business plan and development plan for the Rural Regeneration Company would involve key challenges in maintaining the commitment of the partners and stakeholders. We would concur with that view and have some concerns that delays in gaining authorisation of the additional funding from Government may result in a loss of momentum.

[115] The proposals also conform with the *UK Biodiversity Action Plan* (1994); *Strategy for Sustainable Land Management* (2001); *Hills Task Force Report* (2001); *England Forestry Strategy* (1998); and *National Parks as Test-beds for Rural Revival* (2001).

[116] Data from Peck, F., Bell, F. and Connolly, S (2002) *Mid-Term Review of Partnership Working in West Cumbria.* Centre for Regional Economic Development, University of Northumbria.

[117] Oral evidence from John Dunning and Ray Kessler of the NWDA.

[118] These are also known as 'action research' programmes. They involve undertaking research as a 'live' development project, where the participants gain the knowledge and information from the research process as the project progresses. At the same time, the research results can be disseminated to a wider audience so stimulating uptake of the findings.

[119] This is the significant thrust of the *Sustainable Landscapes for Cumbria* Action Plan developed by the Landscape Regeneration Sub-group of the Cumbria FMD Task Force.

[120] Submission by the Royal Society for the Protection of Birds. This included the report by Gaskell, P., Clark, M. and Mills, J. (2000) *Sustainable Environment and the Farm Business – Cumbria Farm Link.* Countryside and Community Research Unit, University of Gloucestershire.

[121] Forestry Commission (2002) *Cumbrian Woodlands – Taking Forward the Cumbrian Woodlands.* Framework Business Plan 2002-2005.

[122] Cumbria has three designated Areas of Outstanding Natural Beauty outside the two National Park areas. These are the Solway Coast, Arnside and Silverdale, and the North Pennines.